The Late Ha

Turkey Times, Past and Present

Patricia Graham (*née Peele*)

Best Wishes

Pat Graham

Printed by Barkers Print & Design Ltd
Attleborough, Norfolk.

ISBN 978-0-9554543-8-7

Photographs on cover - four generations of the Peele family. From top left, clockwise; Ernest (in white coat) and George Peele, Patricia Graham (née Peele), Frank and Gertrude Peele, James Graham.

The Norfolk Black Turkey logo on following page is copyright Peele's Norfolk Black Turkeys, www.peelesblackturkeys.co.uk

Cover design and book layout by Rachel Rusholme Pilcher, kea designs.

Acknowledgements

A big thank you must go to Rachel Rusholme Pilcher for helping put together this book. A task that she has willingly undertaken and given her valuable advice and assistance.

My thanks also go to the staff of the Gressenhall Rural Life Museum for scanning photographs in an album originally belonging to George Peele, donated by the family to the museum.

Other photographs and information, where acknowledged have been used with the kind permission of the Eastern Daily Press, and the Attleborough Heritage Centre. Extracts from diaries belonging to the Dennis family, Bob Curson and the book entitled, 'The Deserted Medieval Village of Thuxton, Norfolk' by Peter Wade-Martins and Lawrence Butler (EAA 46, 1989) have all added to the information, as has the valued input from my sister Diana, Hilda Edwards and Yvonne Fransham of Pettits and my family and friends.

Pat Graham
2011

Foreword

As you read the story that unfolds on these pages you will realize that we have in Peele's a food business like very few others. It is no exaggeration to describe it as a national treasure.

At any point in their history, their heads could have been turned towards the ruthless pursuit of profit at the expense of everything else, including the turkeys; but they have persisted in their beliefs and not only maintained a breed of turkey that was being lost in the rapid advance towards the cheap and mass production of food, but they have ensured that a truly remarkable piece of meat maintains its place on the Christmas dinner plate.

A few years ago, I made a television programme in which we were recreating the values and practices of traditional farming. We went to Peele's at hatching time and found a farm where little can have changed in decades. If those old ancestors, so evocatively pictured in this book, were to reappear now, they'd still recognize much that goes on. It is not that they do things in an old-fashioned way, it's rather that they do them in the best possible way for Peele's have realized that the best way to grow turkeys is the old way of doing it.

I have never cared much for livestock factory farming. It has given us apparently cheap meat, but in truth the cost has been dear. It has forced farmers to ignore their natural instincts of animal and land husbandry, and made consumers indifferent to the methods used to put food on their plates. It has also brought about the demise of some precious breeds of farm animal, all good servants but now extinct. But Peele's has kept the connection. I saw it in the way the birds were hatched, reared, and fattened. I came away from their farm with the feeling that those in charge knew every one of their birds, and treated them with the respect they deserved.

In return, customers come back to Peele's year after year for their turkey because they know that, in some way, the attention that is given to the growing birds works its way deep into the flavour of the meat on the plate. How that works I do not fully understand, but I am certain it is true. Perhaps it is down to honesty: a decent bird given a decent life gives you something that a less sensitive way of farming can never provide.

Perhaps its history gives it a flavour as well. The story of Peele's goes back over many generations of farming folk in Norfolk and this book is as much a tale of the changing face of Norfolk farming. There was much in the old farming days that we were well rid of: worker exploitation, poor pay and housing. But not everything in a traditional farming system need be consigned to the bin of history. Peele's have been clever in seeing what was worth preserving and have kept it alive. That's their secret.

The Norfolk Black Turkey is a prince amongst table birds and Peele's are the kings of the turkey business. Together they make for a fascinating story.

Paul Heiney
Suffolk
November 2010

Contents

Introduction

A motto written on a silk book marker found in my grandmother's bible reads,

'I shall pass through this world but once. Any good thing therefore that I can do or kindness that I can show to any human being or dumb animal, let me do it now. Let me not deter it or neglect it. For I shall not pass this way again.'

My grandmother, Eleanor Peele, passed away in her 69th year on 19th September 1941. Her gravestone reads, *'We shall remember while the light lasts and in the darkness we shall not forget'*.

This book is dedicated to the memory of my grandparents, parents and the many characters and situations that touched their lives and mine since the 1900s. The family coat of arms with the words 'Industria', sums up the generations of Peeles connected with farming since the 17th century. Various branches of the family, once yeoman farmers, became mill owners, parliamentarians and even Prime Minister.

Our branch of the family have always been farmers and noted for Peele's turkeys since 1880. My father, Frank Peele was known for his saving of the Norfolk Black turkey from extinction and the promotion of the breed, claiming that Thuxton was the 'Home of the Norfolk Black Turkey.' He was a founder member of the British Turkey Federation in 1951 and President of the Norfolk Branch until his death in 1980. He was followed by Bernard Matthews as president.

Photographs, handed down through the generations in the past 130 years of business, have made it possible to illustrate this book. It follows the family from the Victorian era to the present day, giving details of life on the farm through the seasons of the year with the help of my sister, Diana, farm foreman Bob Curson, and family diaries. As well as stories of encounters with television and the media.

I must thank my children, James and Janette, for the encouragement to put this project together, thereby giving a historical record of events to hand down to the next generation.

Pat Graham
2011

James and Janette on Peele's Norfolk Black turkey stand at
The Royal Norfolk Show.

Chapter 1

1945 - The Coming of Bess

It was a moonlight night, one of those nights where there is no wind and only a few puffy clouds float across in the stillness of the moonlit sky. A night where the sounds of dogs barking in the distance, the tawny owl screeching its cry and even the smallest sound seemed so scary.

Blossom and Bess.

Mother and Father appeared to be worried about the animals, the cart horses in particular and as I was only a child of six years old, this disturbed me. Blossom, an almost white ancient Percheron cart horse, plus others that worked on the land at Rookery Farm, Thuxton, were squealing, snorting and charging around the front meadow. Their hooves were thundering on the dry ground making a fearful noise. I was ushered up to bed early and told not to go outside or I might get trampled on. I could hear the neighbour's voice and my parents discussing what action was to be taken. After what seemed to be an eternity to my young ears, all became quiet. The stillness of the evening with the twinkling stars and moonlight shining through the half closed curtains, resumed casting its eerie shadows on my bedroom wall. Eleven months later and me a little wiser to the situation, I was told that Blossom and the other two mares were having babies. The neighbour's stallion had broken out on that moonlight night, eleven months previous, and put Blossom and the other mares in foal. The neighbour whose stallion had caused the trouble, lent Father a horse to cart the muck and move the turkey folds during the time that Blossom and the others were nursing their foals. In 1941, Father had bought two old Fordson tractors and made one workable tractor which quickly found a use of ploughing and doing the heavy jobs. With the mares out of action, the Fordson tractor was soon joined by more Fordsons to work the 157 acre unit.

I called Blossom's foal, Bess. She was a dark grey dappled filly and full of fun. As a child, I had no fear of these huge horses and sometimes sneaked into the cobbled horse stable with its heavy wood stalls to watch Charlie Page, the team man, who when the horses went from the farm became the head poultry man. At the end of the day, when Blossom had finished moving turkey folds or carting muck, Charlie would feed Blossom with crushed oats and bran from the large iron bins. These had swing tops on them to keep out the rats. Then he would fill the cast iron horse rack with sweet smelling meadow hay and give Blossom a quick brush down and a pat as appreciation for a good day's work.

Many a child has been kicked and killed by cart horses frightened when tied up in the stable and I, 'Miss Paddy', was soon told by Charlie Page to 'KEEP OUT.' This did not stop me from sneaking through the barbed wire fence when Bess was about two years old and quite a big chunky Percheron horse, to give her some titbits like lumps of sugar I had smuggled from the house. On my way back through the barbed wire, my woollen cardigan got caught and I was hung up. Bess thought she would investigate my predicament and started nuzzling and pulling my pigtails! Mother, having heard my cries, came bustling from the kitchen and soon unhooked me with a severe ticking off.

Charlie Page holding Paddy.

Blossom moving water cart near turkey folds.

It was not long after that Father invested in more tractors and the days of the horses were numbered. No more sitting astride the creaking wooden saddles on these gentle giants as they pulled the carts down the yard or watching and hearing them clip clop to the farm pond situated inside the farm gate, to water at the end of the day.

Bess was sold to Geoffrey Peacock of Morley who was an old school friend of my father. Mr Peacock's horseman, Jack Juby, then finished breaking Bess into work. Father and Charlie had started on this process by making Bess pull a large log of wood around the front meadow. This spared the valuable machinery getting damaged when pulled by a young horse. It also taught her to feel the harness and weight dragging behind her back legs and to obey to the words of command, 'gee up etc'.

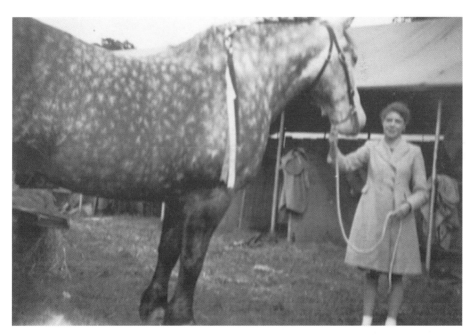

Paddy leading Bess at The Suffolk Show.

A few years after Bess was sold to Geoffrey Peacock, I visited the 1952 Suffolk Agricultural Show with my parents and Mother and I made straight to the heavy horses. There we found Jack Juby with an array of rosettes attached to the Percherons he had shown that day for the Peacocks. To my delight they had taken along Bess for the novice class. She seemed to remember me. Jack soon found me a job of leading her around the grand ring for the parade of heavy horses. My footwear of sandals and dress was not really suitable for the occasion, but Bess and I followed Jack with his prize winning Percheron mare around the ring to the applause of the crowd.

There were times when some horses on farms did not receive the grooming and attention that happened with Mr Peacock's horses and my father's. I remember hearing how Father obtained a skinny, rough looking horse full of mange and lice and soon had it looking fit again. He used an old remedy of putting snuff in warm cows' milk and washing the horse all over with this concoction. The theory was that the lice fed on the milk, taking in the snuff which made them sneeze and this in time killed them. A photograph, taken with my first Kodak camera, of Blossom and Bess, is a reminder of my happy childhood days on the farm.

Chapter 2

'Up Corn, Down Horn'

There were six men working on our farm when I was growing up. Like all mixed farms during and after the war, there was a herd of cows to be milked by hand which took two men and Father several hours in the day to milk, feed, clean out the cowshed and bed down with straw. In 1934, the milk was put in big 17 gallon metal churns. Father would take the milk to the Wymondham dairy and, on the same journey, my sister to Lyndhurst School in Wymondham. On school holidays and when at the age of ten, my sister Diana went to Dereham Secondary School, the churns of milk were taken to the local railway station at Thuxton to be transported to Wymondham. Later when dairies started collecting by lorry, the churns became ten gallons in volume and were made of an alloy to make them lighter and easier to handle. Wooden stands or anything that made a platform would be seen on the side of the road near farm driveways. These stands were for the milk churns to be stood on so that the lorry driver could manhandle them on to a flat lorry and leave the same number of empty churns for the next day's milk. Some stands had shelters built over the top to keep the sun from shining on the milk. There was no refrigeration then and the milk would soon go sour. After the Second World War, our milk went to the dairy at Attleborough, where several years later I did my practical experience, working in the laboratory before going to a college to learn dairy farming.

It was always considered that cows and beef animals were a must on a farm. If the corn prices were good, then the beef price would be bad and vice versa. The old saying of 'Up corn, down horn'. The bank manager was always pleased to see 'horn' on a farm, knowing full well that there was something of immediate value to help pay the bills. I remember being told that Father had the bank manager call and demand that Polly, the best cow in the herd, was to be sold. Ernest Peele, my grandfather, enjoyed gambling and cards, rather than hard physical work and his overdraft situation had to be sorted out. Consequently Father had to sell the best cow at Norwich market to clear some of the debt. In the 1930s, the bank manager was a highly respected and educated man like the rector, doctor and schoolmaster. The local school for Thuxton was at Garveston and was built in 1876. Like many villages, Thuxton, a small hamlet off the B1135, once had a village shop and post office run by the Softly family, a railway station, a police house, an ale house thought to be the 'Adam and Eve' or 'Red Bull' and a church. The latter still open for services once a month.

Bricked cottages on left thought to be a private ale house called the 'Adam and Eve' or the 'Red Bull'.

It is thought the ale house was Number 6, one of six cottages built in the 1800s on land owned by Rob Wortley, according to the enclosure map of 1811. In the tithe map details of 1844, John Ward and others lived in these cottages and might have brewed beer in Number 6, now Horse Shoe Cottage and Number 5 Seaman's Cottage, which are the only ones still standing. In the early 1900s this area was owned by the Seaman family, with a cottage and small farm on the corner of Hingham Road, now part of a field.

It was the story of the ale house that Bill Abel remembered in the early 1920s when he lived with his sisters and parents on a smallholding at Riverside, Tanners Green in Garveston. Whilst living at Tanners Green Bill contracted polio as a child, after falling into the nearby river. The polio left him lame, but aided by a built up boot, he was able to live and work his whole life with the cows at Rookery Farm.

As a boy leaving school, he went to help my father for a fortnight while the cowman Len Whitehand was off sick with shingles. Previous to this, Mother had rescued Len from a rampaging bull by sending her little Jack Russell dog into the field to distract the bull while she pulled Len under the fence. Some 40 years later, Bill Abel, after working on the farm milking cows first with Len Whitehand by hand and then later mastering the use of bucket milking machines, had to retire. A tumour found on his brain meant operations and surgery and the dairy herd at Rookery Farm, was sold in 1972.

Billy Abel moving twin friesian calves outside the old granary at Rookery Farm.

I owe my interest in dairy cows to Bill Abel. As a child in my woollen siren suit and hat (hand knitted) by Mother, I played in the cowshed, insisting that I should be tied up in the large wooden stalls with a chain tied around my neck, just like the cows. When it came to feeding in the cowshed, my little trolley would be piled high with hay dollies I had made as a special treat for the cows. The trolley would sometimes be used to pull big wicker skeps holding chopped straw and mangolds, a kind of beet looking like a huge round golden turnip. Linseed cake which was brought to the farm in big flat slabs would be put through a cake crusher and sprinkled on the straw and chopped mangolds. Big tubs of sticky sweet black molasses were also used as part of the cow's diet in the 1940s and many a finger tried this gooey sweet stuff with a slice of tasty moist mangold! The thought of disease and dirt never entered the mind, as what was edible for animals must be good for humans too! When I think how cows were kept up to the mid 1900s, riddled with tuberculosis (TB) and udder diseases, it is a wonder how so many people survived.

Cows were kept in small herds on nearly every farm and milked by hand. According to space and labour, a 30 cowherd would have been considered large. The cowshed at Rookery Farm, Thuxton, dated back to the mid 1800s and was an L shaped brick building, part of a range of buildings put up in Victorian times. Two cows would be tied with chains around the neck and stand side by side within wooden stalls with brick mangers in front for the food. The standing area was bedded with straw and raised up from the area at the back where the dung would collect. The cows were let out to water from the pond near the farm entrance or from a big cast iron water tank, which was half of a ship's boiler that stood in the exercising yard. This smelly stone and mud area enclosed by buildings contained the dung heap and old sump that collected the dirty cow urine and water. A prolific growing elder tree had made its home in the sump which was covered or not with rusty tin. In the summer, when the cows were out to grass, the old broken railway sleepers which were meant to act as a solid surface leading into the cowshed entrance, would become green and slimy with cows muck. This disgusting, slippery green mess and dung heap nearby, with its discarded straw bedding, attracted the many types of gnats and flies which acted as immediate food for the martins and swallows that nested around the house and buildings.

Each cow knew the correct stall to go into and would proceed in through the end door and fill up the stalls waiting to be tied up by a chain or yoke around the neck - sometimes pinching a mouthful of another cow's food on the way in. The bull was quiet, not like his predecessor and usually came in last and was housed at the far end of the cowshed. He was a handsome Red Poll which, although my parents did not know, Bill would give me a ride on his back into the cowshed! The cows were a motley collection of English breeds; Shorthorn, Red Poll, and Friesian. Many were cross breeds with curling horns and long teats for hand milking. This operation took place by sitting on a home made three legged stool one side of the cow, near the back legs and tucking your head, covered with an old cloth cap into the flank of the cow. The warmth of the cow in the winter after a late night out would soon send the milker to sleep, only to be woken by the cow raising her foot and kicking the milk over the floor!

There was much to be desired in terms of hygiene. The old time milkers would spit on their hands to make the purchase and slip required to make the milk flow. Hair and muck gained in the process would be excluded from the pure warm golden milk when the contents of the hooded bucket were drained through a muslin cloth and put over a cold water filled corrugated cooler and into a churn. This milk was pure with all its fat content intact. About two gallons each day would be set aside in flat enamel pans to naturally cool and let the fat rise as cream for butter making. The next day a skimmer was used. The fat was skimmed with a flat metal type dish with small holes in it to let the white watery milk through and save the fat. The skimmed milk was then fed to the few Large Black or Essex Saddleback pigs as slop. This was a mixture of barley meal finely ground and dunked in the spare skimmed milk. The pigs certainly loved this treat and would squeal and grunt their appreciation. The pigs were my mother's pin money and a way of getting some extra cash to use around the house when the piglets were sold as fat.

Pigs, contrary to what people might think, are very clean animals and keep an area of the sty for bedding and an area for feeding and also for dunging. During and after the Second World War, a pig would be killed and stored in the cellar on the old marble slabs. After hanging for a few days, the sides would be salted, brined and smoked and made into bacon. This was then hung in an old pillow case or muslin cloth on a hook from the ceiling in the spare room where it was cool and dry. The resulting bacon with its rind of fat would hang there for months, only being handled when slices were required. There was always several nights feed of homemade sausages when a pig was killed, plus the lovely flavour of fresh liver and pluck with home-grown mashed potatoes.

Mother grooming her Large Black pig by the dog kennel.

It became compulsory in the 1940s to test all cattle for TB. A disease that was rife in this country passed from cows' milk to humans - hence the introduction of pasteurization. Out of the herd of 22 cows, plus some calves at Thuxton, only six young female animals were clear of the disease. So the old wooden stalls were removed and concrete floors and metal partitions took their place. In 1947 Father automated to Alfa Laval bucket milking machines. Billy took over the cows and Father hastily retired from milking. My favourite cow Bluebell, which I had learnt to milk by hand at an early age, failed the TB Test and was slaughtered.

Chapter 3

Rookery Farm and the village of Thuxton

My parents moved to Rookery Farm, Thuxton in 1932. At this time the land around the house was rough grazing with hollows that held the water in winter. There were brick buildings, laid out around an open courtyard so that different breeds of animals each had their own shed or space, but the farm did not begin life this way.

1955, aerial photo of Rookery Farm, Thuxton.

It is likely that Rookery Farm was named for the rooks that nested in the trees in the drift way that once joined the village of Thurstanton to Thuxton. From 1845 for the next 50 years, but not recorded in 1903, White's Directories give details of one of the finest oaks in the county, being over 700 years old on Rookery Farm. By looking at old records and maps held in the Archives and Records Office in Norwich, I have traced the previous owners of Rookery Farm back from the Enclosure map of 1811, when Charles Heyhoe farmed 100 acres. This map shows a small house; presumably a cottage type dwelling with a kitchen and living area downstairs and bedrooms above. It shows a small building away from the house and then a large long building just inside the farm entrance as you enter on the right. This is where in my young days the pond for watering the horses was. Perhaps the building on the map by the road was for horses and carts and not a permanent structure.

White's directory of 1834 describes Thuxton as having 1200 acres with 83 inhabitants living in scattered farm houses and cottages. The land of Thuxton Manor belonged to Lord Wodehouse of Kimberley Hall, whose family can be traced back to a knight who fought at Agincourt for Henry V in 1415. Thuxton Wace's Manor belonged to Edward Lombe Esq. Geo. Holman and R & W Palmer are noted as occupying their own estates. The farmers were listed as John Taylor of High House and Caleb Vasser of Rookery Farm. Later, in the tithe apportionment of 1844, the owner of the house and buildings is listed as Anne Maria Butcher with the same occupier - Caleb Vasser. Anne Maria Butcher was married to Robert Butcher, a farmer and corn merchant from Bungay. On the exterior wall at the kitchen end of Rookery Farm a diamond shaped plaque has the date 1850 and the initials 'AM RB', presumably representing the names of Anne Maria and Robert Butcher. As owners of the property it is thought that they built an extension onto the front of the house, along with the brick farm buildings and barn. Looking at birth records and the census of 1841, Caleb Vasser, the farmer, occupied the house and had an ever increasing family during the 1830s. It was during this time that an early Victorian manor type farm was built with the house being extended and stables and sheds built for horses, cattle and sheep that grazed the 100 acres of grassland.

All the meadows were supplied with water tanks made from old cast iron ships' boilers cut in half. The water was pumped up by a windmill to a 1000 gallon tank situated in the top of the barn. This height gave the water enough gravity to reach all the distant pastures. The brick barn, with its wide double doors was used for storing and threshing corn with a steam engine and threshing machine. In the mid 1800s this was a very new labour saving way of threshing, which caused riots amongst the farm labourers. There were cart lodges, cowsheds, calf and goat sheds and horse stables. The gig shed and riding stable for the family were opposite the house. Attached to the old part of the house was a dairy with slate shelves for setting the pans of cream for butter making and a cool shelf for storing food. Next to the dairy was a granary with a wood fired copper or boiler once used for heating the swill and no doubt leftovers from the house. This would have been fed to the pigs in the pigsties opposite. Above the granary was a loft where pigeons were kept and attached to the granary was a home for three goats. A large doomed Dutch barn, with a black corrugated tin roof erected in the late 1800s to protect the hay and straw for animals, stood at the end of the yard near the pigsty.

When I was small, the stack yard with its neat thatched stacks of wheat, barley or oats stood at the end of the yard. This area is now covered by sheds for cattle and machinery. In the 1950s, the stack yard was moved to the corner of the turkey meadow, away from house and buildings in case it ever caught fire. On one occasion a stack full of fresh loose hay overheated and flew afire. It had got hot within the stack and smouldered inside for several days before it finally flared up. An iron bar would normally be put in the stack of hay to see what temperature the inside was. On this occasion the stack had not been checked. With no mains water and the deep bore well some distance away in the farm yard, the fire brigade had to use the ponds which soon ran dry. The stack was finally allowed to bum out. Before the Fire Service was formed, it was the various insurance companies that attended fires. A sign for the particular company that insured the premises would hang on the house or barn wall and it was only that insurer that would send a fire tender to put out the fire. The farm was insured with the Atlas Insurance Company and had a sign hanging on both the house and the barn.

White's Directory of 1854 refers to the Taylor family as farmers of High House and landowners of Rookery Farm, having taken over the ownership from Anne Marie and Robert Butcher. In 1832 Alice Lydia Taylor, daughter of John Taylor, a Norwich solicitor who farmed at High House in Thuxton married Francis Oddin Taylor from Winfarthing. In 1876, Francis Oddin Taylor, sold Rookery Farm to a John Franklyn of

Terrington St. Clements for £5,900. This deal failed and the depressed years of the 1880s and 1930s saw the farmhouse and land change hands several times from Robert Abbot to Timothy Coleman and back to the Abbot family. This family traded as 'Abbot Bros.' and lived at the farm from 1880 to 1932. In 1880, Robert Abbot, a dealer in farm livestock moved from Kirby Lonsdale, Westmorland, to Rookery Farm and used the railway to send livestock all over the country. Robert Abbot was grandfather to Jack Abbot, who carried on the Abbot Bros. livestock firm and whose son, Morris Abbot now lives at the Villa. The Abbot family retained the two cottages and an orchard once attached to the farm (together now known as Rookery Villa) when in 1923 the Capitol and Counties Bank took over Rookery Farm as trustees. In 1932, my father Frank Peele rented it from the bank until after World War II, when with improving profits in agriculture he was able to buy the farmstead.

The Abbot Bros. traditional poultry huts used to cover the orchard, but have now been cleared away, and the various breeds of poultry and ducks that once inhabited the area, have given way to a pleasant well trimmed area of grass. In 1906 they won the cup for the best turkey in the Grand International Show at Olympia in London. It is said that Jack Abbot's father, Henry (Harry), had a special mahogany wood surround mantelpiece built in Rookery Farmhouse in his office, to display the various cups that the family had won with their livestock.

Jack Abbot was known for his dealings in anything from poultry, pigs, goats, cattle, ferrets and pigeons to land. Various breeds of poultry and goats were often seen parcelled or tied to the railings at Thuxton Station waiting to go by train all over the country. Sometimes they strayed over the road to Rookery Farm. The Abbots dealt in many breeds of poultry including golden pheasants, turkeys and Muscovy ducks. I well remember a Muscovy duck hatching her chicks near the farm pond on our side of the road and then taking her brood back to the Villa, but two ducklings got left behind. As a child I played near the farm pond and spotted the two orphan ducklings. I plagued my sister to rescue them and they were duly put in a shoe box and kept warm on the side of the brick copper in the kitchen. The new family additions soon grew being fed on turkey food and developed into a duck and drake. The next year the duck hatched 16 little fluffy yellow ducklings under a turkey shed. Father was not amused as I spent most of my holiday time directing the new family to the corn shed where mum and babes had a good fed of wheat! The Muscovy drake became quite aggressive to my parents, but not to me. Perhaps he realised I was just looking after his family.

Jack Abbot gave Thuxton its village sign which was repainted by inmates of a local prison. The sign is now in the centre of the village, on the pocket sized green near the church. The church, in parts dates back to the Saxon period and has witnessed the changing centuries.

St. Paul's Church, Thuxton.

The font is purported to be Norman, set on Victorian Purbeck marble legs. The delicately carved wooden pulpit is Jacobean. Brasses on the chancel wall behind the choir stall read 'John Futter of Thuxston, gentleman ob. 1572. Mary (Suffowle) second wife to Gregory Pagrave ob. 1578 and Katherine (Pigeon) third wife of Gregory Pagrave ob. 1596'. The Charles I plaque dated 1637 hanging above the heavy oak door escaped

19

the devastation of Cromwell's men a few years later. In fact the small church, which once was much bigger and had a side aisle, has so far survived invasion and wars.

Thuxton Post Office and shop.

Within Thuxton itself, the 30 or so houses that now stand in the village are mainly positioned around the church. There is a row of cottages between the railway line and church which were once part of Wace's Manor.
The first cottage acted as the local shop and post office until Mrs Softley retired in the 1970s. This shop contained all the basic ingredients for everyday life; tea, sugar, flour etc. During the week the local Eastern Daily Press paper would come by train and was left at Thuxton station to be collected by Bill Abel or someone passing that way, to get it to the farm. The railway, now known as the Mid Norfolk Line is operated by volunteers as a pleasure route and runs from East Dereham to Wymondham. Originally the rail route ran from Wells to Norwich, with changes at Wymondham to pick up the London or Peterborough lines.

Wace's Cottages. (Post Office and shop on left)

This Great Eastern line was axed in 1969 by the then transport minister, Dr. Richard Beeching. When the rail line was developed in 1852 it split the village in two halves. By 1912, Thuxton had a platform and station house, but Garveston, the adjoining village, had no platform. The floods of 1912 washed away the railway bridge at Thuxton that spans the River Yare. The station porter managed to stop an oncoming train from near disaster.

The house and buildings of Rookery Farm were built on what was once the medieval village of Thuxton. Evidence of this settlement was discovered on an aerial photograph taken by the RAF in 1946. Digs in 1963/64 and a subsequent book produced by the Norfolk Archaeological Unit, entitled 'The Deserted Medieval Village of Thuxton, Norfolk' by Peter Wade-Martins and Lawrence Butler about an area next to the farm, confirmed there was once a large linear settlement with a moated manor at the east end of the village towards Runhall.

Children watching for trains at Thuxton Station.
(Photograph courtesy of EDP)

In the Domesday Book of 1086 there were two villages. Thuxton, meaning Thurferd's tun or farm was the largest – with its own church. The other village was called Thurstanton meaning Thurston's tun or farm. These are both Norse names. It has been suggested that maybe two brothers farmed these settlements in the 10th century, side by side. At this time, the ownership of the land was divided unevenly between the King, William de Warenne, Roger Bigod, Hermer Ferrars and Ely Abbey. The lands of Thurstanton were divided between The King and William de Warenne with the abbey of Ely holding rights in both settlements. The church fell within the land of Roger Bigod in Thuxton. The eventual merging of both settlements into one (which became known as Thuxton) was facilitated through having landowners in common between both villages. Over the next four centuries, new and distinct tenures of these areas were carved out through subinfeudation (the practice of sub-letting or alienating parts of land held by a tenant under the king or other superior lord). Butler and Wade-Martins give more detail on these tenures and the framework of the Domesday manors across the two settlements in their volume,

22

East Anglian Archaeology, 1989: 46, 'The Deserted Medieval Village of Thuxton, Norfolk'.

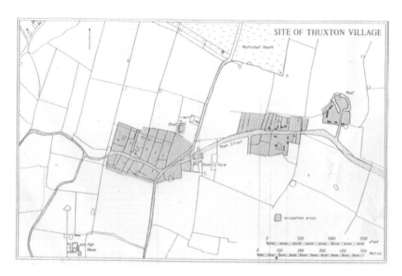

Plan of medieval Thuxton, reproduced with thanks to Peter Wade-Martins.

By the 14th century Thurstanton (referred to as Thurston) was no longer recorded as a separate settlement. The area was now known as Thuxton with three principal landowners owning moated homesteads. It is thought that Thomas Bardolf owned Wace's manor near the church; Richard de Thurston, a manor at the east of the village, part of the Kings holding and Manor of Swathing in Hardingham Parish and part of Bigod manor, later owned by the Wodehouse family. The third owner was John de Thurston whose moated residence was near Rookery Farm. Traces of this moat can be found in the grounds of what is now Rookery Villa. The pasture opposite Rookery Villa was once called Black Close, suggesting it may be associated with the Black Death of 1349 which decimated the population of many towns and villages and left fewer labourers to work the land for the manors. Those that did survive demanded higher wages and in 1379 there were 39 recorded inhabitants in Thuxton paying the Poll Tax, a tax that in 1381 sparked the Peasants Revolt.

By the 15th century the ownership and redistribution of arable acres around

High House and Rookery Farm had extinguished the open field system of agriculture and strip farming and pushed cottagers to the margins of cultivated land and towards Mattishall Heath. With less area to carry on their subsistence way of farming and the collapse of the wool trade, the remaining families moved away from the area, causing part of the village to die out. The houses made of clay lump, wattle and daub disintegrated with the ravages of time and went back to natural vegetation, leaving humps under the grass and dips that held the water in winter where the roads ran between the houses. It was these features that showed up in the aerial photograph of 1946. In the 1960s the government gave grants to farmers to drain and clear land and bring back areas like this to produce more food. It was the clearing of part of this rough ground, owned by the Banham family that enabled Peter Wade-Martins and Lawrence Butler to carry out the archaeological dig of 1963/4, revealing a long lost way of farming and living. After the dig was concluded the land was once more brought back into cultivation, but this time farming with 20th century machinery instead of sheep.

Chapter 4

Farming History and Sir Robert Peel

Farming seems to go in cycles. New inventions and ideas are often a similar way of doing things from previous years but a bit more mechanised. Good inventions often come from the time of war or financial depression when there is a change in circumstances of labour or finances. Also because of changes in agriculture, the movement of farming families and labourers who worked the land have left historical landmarks on our countryside. The life of subsistence farming and the open field cultivation was changed in the 1700s by mechanisation and industry. The Norfolk four course rotation in agriculture was introduced by Viscount Townsend of Raynham. Turnips and swedes were grown in the yearly cycle of crops and gave fodder for cattle and sheep throughout the winter. This enabled the livestock to be kept alive throughout the winter months, instead of being slaughtered in the autumn and the carcasses salted to be used later. Lord Coke of Holkham Hall also practised a four course rotation of wheat, swedes and turnips, oats or barley, and in the fourth year; rye grass and clover, the latter helping to fix nitrogen in the soil ready to give the wheat crop much needed nutrients for the start of the next four year cycle.

Robert Bakewell was a pioneer of stock breeding for food quality, which prior to this date had seen sheep valued for their wool and cattle for their strength to pull ploughs. By the end of the 18th century, Bakewell had succeeded in the breeding of sheep to produce a good quality carcass and Lord Coke of Holkham not only improved his own flock of sheep but every year held 'sheep shearings' for farmers from all over the country and Europe, to come and witness and learn from his success. Jethro Tull, who is said to have invented the seed drill and horse hoe, also contributed to the acceleration of change in agriculture. The seed drill allowed the seed to germinate below the surface of the ground and out of reach of the birds and wind, so increasing the yield of grain harvested.

In 1793 Arthur Young was secretary on the newly established Board of Agriculture. He was a great publicist of the scientific change in agriculture but it is said that Young was hopeless at farming. It is recorded in one of Bloomfield's volumes that on a visit to Carleton Rode in Norfolk in 1810 Young found the countryside much changed as he had last seen the area before the Enclosure of the Commons Act for Carleton Rode of 1778. The government brought in this act to enclose and plough the commons thus producing more wheat for bread to feed the ever increasing population. Over the centuries, houses and smallholdings had sprung up on the edge of common land, where the right to gather wood, fruit and graze animals, but not to build or cultivate common land, had been law. With the coming of the enclosure, which took place in villages from the mid 1700s to early 1800s, the thorn hedges and stone walls we see today were the result. These divided the common land into plots which were given to existing farmers to cultivate and produce more wheat. Each plot was surrounded by a ditch with a thorn hedge or stone wall to keep cattle or sheep in or out. The hedge was planted on the soil that was taken out when the ditch was made. Through this our countryside has become the well recognised patchwork of fields and boundaries, with hedgerows often dating back over 250 years.

This change to industrialization and different ways of farming spelt the decline of the wool trade. This once stable wealth had seen men build many fine churches in East Anglia and trade with the continent for many centuries. Industry in the north and Midlands made some families wealthy and other families poor. The latter moved from East Anglia to find work in the factories or went abroad. The social pattern of country life started to change in the 18th century, leaving some villages isolated. Where there had once been a thriving communities living on the edge of common land, grazing a few sheep that provided wool to spin into yarn and sell to make a living, with the advent of the Enclosure Act and subsequent industrialization, families were left without a living and forced into poor houses or to move away from the community. The wool spinners of Norfolk resisted the change to more mechanized ways and still spun their yarn by hand spindle long after the weavers in Essex and Suffolk had declined. By the mid 1800s the mechanical looms in the north were weaving large quantities of cloth with wool taken from sheep now grazing on the hills. The flat lands of Norfolk entered a new era and started to develop into the breadbasket of England.

Tracing my family tree on the Peele side has shown a lineage of farmers and graziers back to 1690 connected with the county of Lincolnshire before moving to Norfolk in 1880. There are very few families recorded living in the East of England who have the surname spelt with an 'e' on the end. Our son was given the name of Peele as a middle name after it was pointed out by my godmother Mary Peele, that he was the first boy born in the direct family for 66 years! According to a book written by Parker in 1891, entitled 'Sir Robert Peel', the name can be traced back to the 16th century and means 'hillock, castlet or fort, formerly an appendage to a baronial residence on the borders of Yorkshire and Lancashire of which two remain, Bolton Peel and Hellifield Peel'. It is thought that the name originated from this area. The name of Peele is also found in America, as several families emigrated in the 1700s.

The story passed down through my family tells that the 'e' was added on to the surname of Peel and we were related to four successive generations of Robert Peel; who each became known for becoming an industrial millionaire, a speaker of the House of Commons, Prime Minister, and the secretary of State for India, respectively. After looking into our family tree, I found the 'e' has been on the name since the 1600s and we were never directly related to the Sir Robert Peel line! Over the centuries, the name has been spelt in many other ways and altered to 'Peal' and 'Pele', as well as Peel and Peele.

Within the Sir Robert Peel lineage, it was Robert (Parsley) Peel, who reportedly dropped the 'e' from the family name. He thought the family was too prevalent in Lancashire and Yorkshire and that the extra 'e' was obsolete and unnecessary! Thereafter the Peel family, now with the 'e' dropped, became a voice in history. The descendants of Robert (Parsley) Peel's father, William, went from being farmers, combining wool weaving with agriculture, to expanding into manufacture and mechanical inventions and eventually parliament. Just before Robert (Parsley) Peel died in March 1792, he applied for a family coat of arms, not merely for himself but for the descendants of his father, William Peele. Note at this

27

point in time, the 'e' is still part of the name.

The coat of arms is described as '*argent three sheaves of as many arrows proper, bonded gules on a chief azure, a bee volant or crest, a demi-lion rampant argent collared azure holding a shuttle*'. The bundles of arrows were adopted as an emblem of family unity and the bee and the shuttle as symbols of industry and manufacture. The motto, 'Industria', with its double sense of work and trade repeated the dominant theme, not only of the arms, but of the man to whom they were granted.

Chapter 5

Peele's Norfolk Turkeys

The Peele family tree, with the 'e', goes back to a William Peele of Saxby St. Helen in Lincolnshire who had a son Thomas Peele born in 1690 and farmed at Scothern in Lincolnshire. He married Ann Newell and produced several children. There were two sons from this marriage; William, born 1720 and Richard, born 1734, both of Grayingham in Lincolnshire. The son of William Peele, born in 1753 and also called William married a Jane Wheelwright, who died in 1778 after bearing two daughters. Then William Peele married a second time to his cousin Elizabeth Peele, the daughter of Richard Peele. William and Elizabeth farmed at Gt. Gonerby and Long Sutton. Their son Richard Peele born 1786, was a farmer and landowner at Long Sutton who married Mary Lamb. From this marriage a son named Thomas Lamb Peele was born in 1814 and became a well known farmer in Long Sutton (The Peele family tree can be found in the appendix).

The Peele Community College situated in the parish of Lutton was built on land once owned by Thomas Lamb Peele and is now the secondary school for the area. Thomas married Eliza Cartwright and had 12 children. The oldest son was named Edwin Peele Peele, taking the surname of his great grandmother Elizabeth Peele, as a second Christian name as was the custom in the 1800s. Edwin was educated and became a chemist at Long Sutton, Lincolnshire. The family owned several acres of land around that area and through marriage integrated into the Cartwright, Dennis and Dring families. Emma Harriet Dring married Edwin Peele Peele in 1863. Looking at family silver handed down to my parents, I discovered some silver spoons with the initials of EPP on the handles. I now know they stood for Edwin Peele Peele.

Due to the recession in agriculture in the 1880s, land in Norfolk, Suffolk and Essex, once the sheep and wool producing area of England, was cheap to buy or rent. Many families from Scotland and other parts of the country moved south to seek better land and fortunes. In 1881, my husband's grandfather, William Graham, moved with his cattle and belongings by train from Newton Stewart in Scotland to Essex, to be near the growing population of London. A similar migration of Scottish farmers to English soil took place in the 1920s when the Alston and Patterson families and others moved to Norfolk. Here they could supply fresh milk and produce direct to the people in the towns.

In 1880 the Drings moved to High House Farm, Brandon Parva and Edwin Peele Peele and his wife (formally Emma Dring) and their nine children moved to Stanfield Hall Farm near Wymondham. Edwin Peele had owned a chemist and wine shop in Long Sutton and was not in good health and died two years after coming to Norfolk. His two eldest sons, my grandfather, Ernest Edwin Peele, born 1864, and John George Peele, born 1865, were left to run the business with their mother Emma.

In the 1870s, photography was a new science and became part of a chemist's job and it was therefore not surprising to find several photos of the Dring and Peele family members in big leather bound, gold framed albums. Henry Dring in Tynemouth Devon, who also became a chemist, produced some lovely sepia toned pictures of the Dring family. I suspect that it was because of this family interest in photography that John George Peele (better known as George) was always willing to have photos taken of farming events happening throughout the year. Through this we have a large collection of photos taken by Tom Nokes and Alfieri during Christmas 1904, 1905, 1912, 1913 and 1916 that reflects the turkey business that George and Ernest started, known as 'Peele's Norfolk Turkeys'.

George Peele found the woods that belonged to Stanfield Hall Farm were ideal for rearing bronze turkeys and this wood is still known locally as 'Turkey Wood'. The turkeys were bred and fattened for Christmas and transported to London in a 'rough plucked' state. Feathers were left around the neck, hocks and a few on the back and then the birds were packed in large wicker railway hampers onto a drug or trailer which was pulled by a steam traction engine. Some consignments were taken to the local railway station to go by train, but in 1913 the turkeys were taken by traction engine to London. The journey to Smithfield in London took about a week, which was much faster than when the birds were driven live to London in the 1600/1700s. The A11 was then about one mile wide and just tracks through trees and waste ground where herds of cattle and flocks of sheep and poultry trekked their way to the big city.

By 1810 the 'Norfolk Chronicle' reported that six coaches and carriages, each drawn by six horses, were not sufficient to carry all the packages containing Christmas fayre from Norwich to London. The next year the same paper stated that 12 coaches were not adequate. The journey to London at this time took three days and involved ten stages. The birds sold at 1s to 1s 2d per lb. One story often told is that in 1740, Lord Oxford bet the Duke of Queensbury one hundred guineas that a flock of 100 geese would walk from Norfolk to Smithfield near London and arrive before 100 turkeys. The geese won by two days as the turkeys went to perch in the trees each night and the drovers could not move them on. Geese rest on the ground and so the drovers were able to keep them walking. This story was made into a film in the 1990s, with shots being taken on Old Buckenham Common in Norfolk. The geese were housed overnight at Bill Jackson's Telegraph Farm at the nearby village of Carleton Rode.

The first turkeys originated in America and were not the large white feathered birds we see for sale in the supermarket today, but were smaller with bronze or black feather colouration. Fossils of wild turkeys have been found in Pleistocene deposits, dating the ancestry of the bird back more than twelve thousand years and their predecessors have been linked to the Eocene period some 50 million years ago.

The modern domesticated turkey is descended from the wild turkey (*Meleagris gallopavo*), one of the two species of turkey found in the genus *Meleagris*. There are five subspecies of *M. gallopavo* and recent research has indicated at least two occurrences of turkey domestication before the discovery of America (*'Ancient mitochondrial DNA analysis reveals complexity of indigenous North American turkey domestication'. C. Speller, B. Kemp, S. Wyatt, C. Monroe, W. Lipe, U. Arndt and D. Yang. 2010. PNAS. 107: 2807-2812*). One involving the South American wild turkey; likely to have occurred in south-central Mexico, and a second involving Rio Grande/Eastern wild turkey populations, with the subsequent introduction of domesticated stocks into the Southwestern area. For the ancient peoples of the American Southwest and Mesoamerica, which includes the Aztec Empire, turkeys would have been not only a valuable source of dietary protein, but also yielded by-products such as feathers and bones, having both ritual and domestic uses.

Domesticated varieties of the Mexican subspecies (*M. g. gallopavo*) were imported into Spain from America in the early 16th century and spread quickly across the rest of Europe where the turkey's black feather colour and white flesh were further developed. In Spain the turkey was known as the 'Black Spanish', and in France as the 'French Black'. From here, around 1514, the bird was introduced to Britain, where in East Anglia it became known as the 'Norfolk Black'.

It is thought that another subspecies with bronze coloured feathering was imported into England from North America in the 16th century. William Strickland is the man credited with the introduction of this variety to England in 1526. It is reported that as a young man on a voyage to the New World with Sebastian Cabot, Strickland brought back six turkeys to England after trading glass beads with the native Indians for turkeys. From then on King Henry VIII and the rich ate turkey at banquets instead of peacock or swan. In 1550 after several voyages abroad, William Strickland of Boynton in Yorkshire was granted a coat of arms incorporating the turkey and a lectern in the form of a turkey was presented to Boynton Church. Further turkeys brought to England from North America were crossed with the earlier imported Mexican-Spanish derived 'Norfolk Black' breed producing the bronze known locally as the 'Cambridge Bronze'. The black and bronze turkeys introduced to England were reared in East Anglia by small peasant farmers who sold the birds at the yearly autumn sales in October at Aylsham and Attleborough.

There the turkeys were bought by London businessmen and walked by drovers to Smithfield. The turkeys' feet were treated with tar and chopped straw or sand for the journey. Some were even fitted with leather boots!

Eating the grass, waste corn, black berries, acorns and other wild fruit on the way they made the 100 mile journey to Smithfield Common by early December.

Attleborough Station in 1930s when Mr Forder was drover for Ernest Peele of Leys Farm, Attleborough. (Photo courtesy of Attleborough Heritage Centre)

Here they would rest and fatten until being killed on about December 15th and hung before being made ready for the Christmas table. The first entry for turkeys being sold at Smithfield market is in 1555. Before this date the peacock or goose was the main Christmas dish. A century after the improved black turkey had been introduced to England it was taken back by ship to America, by the early settlers to be used in their Thanksgiving feasts. Here it was crossed with the native wild turkey again, producing the oldest American breeds known as; the 'Narragansett', 'Bronze' and 'Slate' turkeys.

A diary dated 1896 kept by George Peele, giving the wages paid to each man on Stanfield Hall Farm and details of the job they did, is an interesting insight into the daily routine of farm life during the year. At the back of the diary are the details of bronze turkeys bought and sold plus the prices. Cocks (male) turkeys never reached large weights. The heaviest being about 20lb due to the confirmation of the carcass.

Bronze stag turkey. (Image copyright, Peele's Norfolk Black Turkeys)

The original shape was like a pheasant, the turkey being akin to a game bird with a long keel and high breast bone enabling the bird to walk and reproduce naturally. In the 1950s the demand for poultry meat and turkey, in particular at Christmas, meant that the pure breeds were hybridized by the method of artificial insemination. By selection of a broader breasted bird the breeders produced turkeys and chickens with less leg length, shorter keel and wider breasts coupled with a faster growth rate. Instead of being hatched in April/May, they could be hatched in July/August to produce a bird large enough for the Christmas table in less time.

In 1957 my Father wrote an article for the Eastern Daily Press (dated 28th June) detailing the history of turkey breeding in Norfolk and promoting the Norfolk Black Turkey. The last paragraph reads, '*Public taste is, of course the most potent influence in determining the type of stock produced for the market. At the beginning of this century families were large and so were ovens, so that the larger breeds of turkey, such as the Mammoth Bronze, predominated. Today, for a number of reasons, the main demand is for the smaller bird. This is the main factor which is bringing out of seclusion the old Norfolk Black. During the First World War this breed almost became extinct, and the only really good specimens to be found in Norfolk were found by Mr. J. A. Christie. In 1936 the Norfolk Black Turkey Club was formed* (disbanded in 1975) *and a register of pure stock was compiled and breed standards were laid down. Many members of the club have bred to these standards ever since.'*

Norfolk Black turkeys in snow.
(Image copyright, Peele's Norfolk Black Turkeys)

Nowadays the older fashioned breeds, known as the 'Heritage Turkey' in America, are now finding popularity in this country as family pets and through the Turkey Club UK (founded in 2001) their gene pool will be retained. This organisation was started by Janice Houghton-Wallace, who kept a few rare breed turkeys as a hobby. She found them so interesting and to have such individual characters when kept outside free range, that

35

she felt an effort should be made to conserve these rare breeds, before they became extinct. Turkey Club UK now has many members keeping all sorts of breeds, mostly as pets. There are show classes for members at poultry and agricultural shows all over the country, with families learning new skills in poultry keeping and watching the turkey chicks grow.

The older, traditional breeds of turkey start laying a clutch of eggs from March onwards which take 28 days to hatch. They take a longer time to grow than the modern bronze or white and need to be nearly 24 weeks old before killing to get a good clean finish by ensuring the feathers come out easily. It was said by my aunt, that for the old fashioned breeds of turkey to be finished for Christmas, they must *taste the April dew*.

Chapter 6

19th Century Diaries

One way to keep a record of day to day events is to write a diary. William Dennis of King John Farm, Hagerby, nr Sutton Bridge in Lincolnshire did just this from 1845 to his death in 1913. It gives a fascinating insight into life in Victorian times, both politically and socially. He wrote about the weather, farm conditions and, later in life, the condition of relatives' farms. His entry on 16th August, 1910 reads, '*Drove over to High Ash Farm, Hethersett and visited Mr. T. Walker for tea and a farm round in the evening, a fair amount of good young stock and good crops of wheat, oats, beans and clover and a large quantity of young pigs. More attention to the garden and it's surroundings would make a pleasant home but the buildings want a cannon ball putting in and blowing to shivers and some new ones erected, which would be a grand thing for a tenant.*' His thoughts recorded in his diaries are quite revealing and forthright!

George Peele and friends in his first 'moto' car.

37

William Dennis was married to Betsy Jane Dring, a farming family from that area. After the Dring, Peele and Harrison families moved to Norfolk in 1880, William Dennis would visit the families and stay at Stanfield Hall Farm, near Wymondham. On one occasion he describes his journey in the new *'moto'* car that George Peele had purchased. When cars were first on the road, it was compulsory to have a man with a flag walk in front of the vehicle, as these new horseless carriages were a danger to the pony and trap, the normal mode of transport. It was 1909 when George took Mr Dennis to Suffolk to see the new farm George had bought. It was Thickthorn Farm at Horham near Eye in Suffolk. In William Dennis's diary he notes that the farm his nephew has bought is a *'satisfactory investment of his mother's capital, having a comfortable homestead, good land close to a railway station and in a nice district at a cost of £18 per acre'*.

September 26th 1901 wedding. George Peele to Ginny Moore.

William Dennis attended the marriage in 1898, of my grandfather, Ernest Edwin Peele, to Eleanor Lewin, a farmer's daughter from the Old Hall, Marlingford and was also at George Peele's wedding, who married Ginny

Moore on September 26th 1901. (A list of the ancestors of Frank Edwin Peele can be found in the appendix).

Stanfield Hall Farm, where the Peele family had moved too from Lincolnshire, was farmed by George and Ernest Peele in connection with their mother, Emma Peele until her death in 1902. The White Hall, now known as Park Farm, Hethersett was owned by Sir Maurice Boileau Bart of Ketteringham Park. My grandfather Ernest rented this farm until 1916 and this is where my father, Frank Peele was born in 1900. The picture of White Hall, Hethersett shows my father as a child dressed in white with his parents and George and Ginny Peele looking on. The white cotton gown that was used for father's christening was made by Chamberlains of Norwich, a shop that once stood opposite the Guild Hall. The gown has been used for family christenings for nearly a century.

In 2002, Lesley Harrison born in 1914 wrote his autobiography of his life in farming. Lesley's grandfather, Matthew Harrison, originated from Newark in Lincolnshire and moved to Norfolk in the late 1800s to manage Hall Farm, Haugham near Attleborough for an uncle. As a farmer and Wesleyn Chapel preacher he named four of his farming sons, Matthew, Mark, Luke and John. (The Harrison family tree can be found in the appendix). Another son, Edward went to the city. Matthew Harrison senior, took over renting White Hall Farm at Hethersett in 1916 after my grandfather, Ernest Peele, moved to Leys Farm, Attleborough.

Lesley writes, '*In those days before the first world war it did not take a lot of money to take over a rented farm. The horse power raised on the farm, the machinery simple and landlords ready to let land to reliable tenants. When the first son wanted to set up in business he was given enough of surplus stock from the fathers farm and cash to set up in a rented farm. If over the years he was able to pay back the debt to the father he was then put in his parents will, but if this was not accomplished he did not stand to benefit and sad to say that was the case with my father, who saw his brothers and sisters receiving sums while he was left out.*'

The White Hall, Hethersett.

White Hall and the adjoining Planet Farm was made up of 130 acres of mainly heavy land on the main Norwich to London road. Matthew Harrison senior and later Lesley's father, also called Matthew, had moved from light loamy land farms which did well for sheep and barley farming but not for wheat. The heavy land that they both went on to rent did not bring them much success with sheep and the way they had farmed and in Lesley's case his father never paid back the debt. Lesley grew up at White Hall until he married Audrey Ringer and then rented Rookery Farm, Besthorpe. He was able to buy White Hall when the landowner Sir Maurice Boileau died and after several years of dairy and poultry farming at Hethersett and Besthorpe he sold White Hall to the Gowings who created Park Farm Hotel and Leisure Centre.

My grandmother, Eleanor Lewin, before she married Ernest Peele, wrote a diary every day which gives a good insight into the general working day of a young Victorian girl who, according to her diary dated 1888-89, practised the piano and art, arranged flowers and sang in Wilby Church and believed in seeing forthcoming strangers in tea leaves! After the death of her mother, Maria, when she was nearly 18, Eleanor's father employed Miss Kirby to be her chaperone and companion. In her diaries, Eleanor said that her father often complained she was lazy and used to strike her.

Father as a child with wheelbarrow on drive of
White Hall. (Now Park Farm)

Within four months from the death of her mother, her father had married Miss Kirby in Norwich. The marriage ended in divorce a year later. Before this Eleanor was told she had to choose between living at Wilby or move to Marlingford to look after five cows, make butter and cook for her two brothers. Eleanor never got on with her grandparents and even her father, Charles Sutton Lewin, after his divorce, turned to smoking and drinking and accused her through a solicitor of embezzling money. Her young life after her mother died was not a happy one.

In 1890 Eleanor's brother Leonard, then 21 years old, hired the Old Hall at Marlingford from the Bird family. Leonard later married Bessie Bird and Raymond, his brother married Maud Bird. The Old Hall is a large rambling house with parts dating back to the 15th century to which many additional rooms and features have been added over the centuries. This large four storied house with its wood panelled rooms, large fireplaces, blackened kitchen range and staircases leading upwards, must have been an imposing responsibility for a young girl to manage. She was 18 when placed in charge of cooking and looking after her two brothers. She soon became the talk of Marlingford when she rescued a bull from the low meadows on her own.

Eleanor was left £200 by her godfather, Frank Leeds, and bought a pony and trap. On one occasion she drove 16 miles to interview a young girl for the job of helping in the house. There are many mentions in her diary of the weather and how it affected the farm as well as the ups and downs of family life. On one occasion she had to nurse her brother after a terrible accident with the horse slipping and falling down in the trap and throwing Leonard over the back, hitting his head on the ground. The shafts of the cart were broken and the horse and Leonard not able to work for several weeks. Another brother, Reginald Lewin emigrated to Canada and letters sent home in the early 1900s tell of his trials to start farming in the inhospitable area of Red Deer, Alberta. With winter temperatures down to minus 50°F and failing crops, he was forced to seek other work in Vancouver. Eleanor was an avid letter writer and took comfort in writing to her friends and to her sister Isobel.

Looking at the entries in my grandmother Eleanor's diaries of 1896, it was the custom to do the washing on Mondays, iron on Tuesdays and make butter on Wednesdays. The quantities of butter made per week varied from 7lb in April, to 25/30lb in September when the cows calved

42

1870s, Peele's Chemist and Wine Shop, Long Sutton.

Early 1900s, Peele family outside Stanfield Hall Farm.

Eleanor, Frank and Ernest Peele advertising mangolds grown with Hadfield's manures.

Ernest Peele and others advertising mangolds grown with Hadfield's manures.

Loading oat sheaves grown with 'Hadfield's Special Manures'.

1905 transport, horse and wagon.

1905, stumpers at Stanfield Hall Farm.

1905, stumpers at Stanfield Hall Farm.

1904, turkeys hanging.

1905, pluckers with baskets of turkeys ready for transport.

1912, grading turkeys at Stanfield Hall Farm.
(Ernest and George Peele on left)

1912, Frank Peele aged 12, helping grade turkeys.

Turkey helpers with Ernest and George Peele standing at back, on right.

Turkey helpers.

1912, turkey helpers with steam engine and motorbike.

1913, George and Ernest Peele (in white coat) outside Stanfield Hall Farm with consignment of turkeys for London.

George Peele's daughters helping load turkeys.

Turkeys being despatched (when this was printed in the local paper in the 1930s it caused heated debate).

Covering turkey baskets ready for transport.

CONSIGNMENT OF NORFOLK TURKEYS. 7 TON. FOR LONDON.

FROM. J.G.PEELE.
WYMONDHAM.
NORFOLK.

Consignment of turkeys leaving the farm.

*1916, Morley Manor. George Peele's daughters.
Left to right, Kathleen, Muriel and Mary.*

*1920s, Kathleen, Muriel and Mary (left to right)
driving turkeys at Morley Manor.*

1916, shooting party. Peeles, Harrisons and Lewins at Morley Manor.

1916, George Peele at Morley Manor.

and produced more milk, making work for the farm workers during the autumn and winter months. The spring and summer months were taken up with sowing crops, making hay for the animals and getting the harvest gathered before the bad weather. Farming is a cycle of yearly events which are controlled by the weather and that in turn is controlled by the time of the year wherever in the world you are.

The Old Hall, Marlingford.

The principles of butter making have not changed since man first found that the globules of butter fat, known as cream, if shaken about for a length of time, would stick together and force the watery part out, leaving particles of a substance we know as butter and the waste called butter milk. Over the years various contraptions have been used from a glass Kilner preserving jar shaken vigorously for several minutes, to glass containers with a paddle turned by a wooden handle for the small house hold quantities. For the larger amounts of butter to be made, a wooden cask mounted on a stand with a handle to turn this barrel contraption (known as the end over end churn) would have been used. Cream that had been skimmed off the milk, which had been set in large shallow pans for the fat to rise, would have been stored in glazed pots and stood in a cool dairy for the cream to mature and ripen. This was crucial for a quick coming of the butter and so too was the temperature of about 50°F (10°C). Too warm and the butter would be soft, too cold and the butter globules would be small and take longer to form. The normal time for turning these big cumbersome churns is about half an hour, but I have personally turned for one and half hours! In the 1960s when most homes were on electricity, an electric butter churn was used. This was a paddle set in a glass container which was moved by an electric motor. Another contraption for larger quantities of butter to be made consisted of a metal circular pan with a lid, the pan being fitted with a rubber hose on the base that in turn fitted over the central paddle of an old Servis top loading washing machine. The paddle rotated back and forth making the cream swill around in the circular pan. I once had a go with my old washing machine but with little success. It was winter when I tried and the cream had not ripened enough and the temperature was too cold.

The buttermilk left after the butter forms, has to be carefully extracted leaving the frail specks of butter behind. These are then washed in cold salt water to gather the grains of butter together to form a lump to which more salt is added. Salt keeps the butter from turning rancid, gives flavour and extends the shelf life. When a large amount of butter was made, a butter worker was used. This was a wooden table like contraption with a wooden toothed roller that was pulled across the butter, so squeezing the excess water out and helping work in the salt, which in turn displaced more water. The final act was to pat the butter into 1 lb elongated lumps with wooden corrugated butter pats (hands) and then complete the job with a trade mark or pattern. Farmers would sometimes pay the vet's bills or the doctor with a few pounds of butter. It was usually sold at the local market, hence the name of butter market or butter cross for buildings found in the centres of small villages or towns.

Before the Milk Marketing Board (MMB) was set up in 1933 to help the sale of milk during the depression of the early 1930s, many farmers, including my parents, made the excess milk into butter as a means of getting payment for the milk.

Studley Dairy College students, 1957-59. Margaret Turner working end over end butter churn, Marion Wells with butter worker. (Lionel Photography)

Farmers also put notices on the side of the road to entice the thirsty cyclist to buy a glass of milk. This rewarded the cash strapped farmers with a few extra pence. The formation of the Milk Marketing Board created an organisation that bought milk from the farmers, arranged for collection to a local dairy where it was processed into glass bottles and distributed to individual households. In the 1980s, milk quotas were introduced throughout the European Union. Our country did not produce enough milk for the population and was forced to buy in milk from other countries but the dairy farmers were still subjected to EU quotas. The MMB with its marketing skills and distribution network was deregulated in 1994 due to the EU monopolies commission and government regulations of 1993 and was finally dissolved in 2002.

This was a great blow to dairy farmers who over the years had been served by an organisation with co-opted dairy producers on the board who understood the pressures of the dairy industry. An organisation which over the years had progressed the hygiene and quality standards of milk. The MMB had brought in pasteurization to combat the scourge of TB disease, quality control of fat and solids in milk, improved the various British breeds of dairy and beef cattle through artificial insemination and set up centres for the collection of semen from good progeny bulls. It had introduced a new cheese called Lymswold made by Dairy Crest and slogans like '*Drinka pinta milk a day*'. The word 'pinta' became a new word for the Oxford dictionary. Now the name of Dairy Crest is the only thing that remains of the old Milk Marketing Board.

Looking through some possessions left by my grandmother, I was intrigued by something called a 'Spy Programme' and I wondered where it fitted into her life. It was while reading her diary dated June 1896 that I discovered she travelled by train on this day to Manchester with Ernest Peele, who later became her husband. They were initially introduced by her friend Harriet Peele, Ernest's sister. According to her diary, Ernest and Eleanor took part in the Catholic Whit Friday procession in Manchester. Afterwards they went to the docks where she saw two large ships on the newly built Manchester ship canal. Two years before, in May 1894, Queen Victoria performed the official opening of this 36 mile canal. At that time it was the longest in the world beating the Suez Canal that was built in 1869. The Manchester canal connected the city with the sea allowing ships to deliver coal and take cloth from the mills for all parts of the world.

My grandmother, Eleanor was a good seamstress like her mother, Maria. In the 1800s women were taught to sew and cook as these were seen as essential life skills and a means to obtain a partner. The diary notes the price of material bought and the making of stockings, presumably from wool. Embroidery done in the long winter nights by candlelight is always a marvel to me. An embroidered map of England and Wales with all the various counties, as they were in the late 1800s was framed and has been handed down through my family. It would have been the work of my great grandmother, Maria Lewin née Newson or my grandmother Eleanor Peele née Lewin.

Eleanor Peele, water diviner.

Eleanor was educated at Kings Lynn Girls School and was an accomplished artist producing fine pencil drawings of a donkey, scenes of water mills and sailing ships, as well as watercolour pictures of flowers. Her sensitivity to nature made her a natural water diviner. This skill was in later life to earn her a few pounds to go towards the housekeeping in the 1930s. Her account book records divining for wells of water at Banham and Old Buckenham to name a few places, and records the depth to find the well of water and the estimated flow.

Her name is mentioned in a book about water divining, where she wrote a chapter on finding the flow of water. She used the traditional hazel stick at first and often found herself the centre of attraction at parties as she could also divine rare metals. Blindfolded and turned around several times, she would be asked to find a gold ring or watch hidden in the lawn. The effect on her health was evident after these events for she would feel very sick. Later in life she used whale bones set in the shape of a fan for divining. This did not have such an effect on the electrical charge through her body. Divining wells and selling a few eggs seemed to be the lifeline for my grandmother during the late 1930s and early 1940s when she and Ernest lived at Leys Farm, Attleborough. She would journey to Norwich in her pony and trap or be seen riding her three wheeled bicycle into Attleborough, wearing the pretty flowered dresses she had made.

Diana and Eleanor Peele biking from Leys Farm to Attleborough.

Ernest was not the astute businessman her father had thought he was, as Eleanor once wrote in her diary. Ernest had a leaning towards betting on the horses, card games and drinking, with trips to London to savour the night life. He was a good sportsman and bowls player and won trophies at Hethersett bowls club and in his early married life, sang and played the piccolo with Eleanor who accompanied him on the piano or guitar while entertaining at local concerts.

It was Ernest's brother George who was the businessman and who bought Downham Grove outside of Wymondham on the old A11 in 1920, and it is from there that my father, Frank Peele, rented and farmed from 1923

48

to when George Peele, in 1932, sold part of the farm for building houses along Tuttles Lane, Wymondham. George gave my parents six weeks to find another property. The Midland Bank provided details of a 100 acre grass farm to rent at Thuxton known as Rookery Farm which the bank had taken over. In 1916 George sold Stanfield Hall Farm and moved to Manor Farm, Morley St. Peter, a farm with a large timber fronted manor house.

This land later in 1965 became part of Morley Agriculture Research station, now known as Morley Agriculture Foundation. The research station originally started in 1909 at Old Catton and then moved to Sprowston, near Norwich, before moving to Morley. The unit researched plant breeding and grew and tested new varieties of corn, sugar beet and grasses. Every year there would be an open day before harvest when farmers could see the new varieties of wheat, barley, oats and sugar beet and the effects of different amounts of fertilizer, sprays and land management. George Peele was successful in farming at Stanfield Hall Farm and Morley, and the Peele family started to become well known for selling 'Peele's Norfolk Turkeys' to London and the East of England.

Mary Harrison née Peele with
bronze stag turkey.

Plucked turkeys hanging at Manor Farm, Brandon Parva.

Hugh Harrison driving bronze turkeys.

In 1932, George divided the business between his son-in-law Hugh Harrison of L. F. and H. F. Harrison of Manor Farm, Brandon Parva, who had married his daughter Mary Peele and his nephew, my father, Frank Peele who had moved that year to Rookery Farm, Thuxton. Ernest and Eleanor, moved from the White Hall to Leys Farm, Attleborough and continued to farm at Leys Farm until 1937 when they retired to a house called Witton (built by Mr Witton) on London Road, Attleborough.

A letter from Ernest to my father, written on September 3rd 1939, describes how my grandfather had taken a trip that day with a friend in a van and had gone *'through Duxford Aerodrome where the planes were on the field all drawn up with pilots all ready to start, everyone at his place. Then coming home saw a large omnibus loaded with children at Newmarket, expect from London. Then at Six Mile Bottom, soldiers just arriving to camp on a field. How many don't know but a whole regiment. Our road is never quiet for transport etc.'* He didn't realise it at the time but this was the start of the Second World War. An accident outside his house is also mentioned in the letter. *'A cart hit the night soil cart and knocked the wheel off careering across the road, grazing the phone post and finished turned over on the bank. It was a miracle no one was hurt. The stench was awful and the muck was all over the place.'* What a smell must have presided over the area the next day!

Eleanor continued to water divine until 1940 and died during the Second World War in 1942. It was then that my grandfather Ernest moved to Thuxton to live with us and my parents found out how much money he owed to various firms. A total of over £3000 had to be paid back, which was a considerable sum of money in those days. His desire to gamble and drink never left him. When my parents were unable to look after him, he was put in a nursing home. But Father always had to pick up the bills for drink and gambling debts when he visited each weekend. During the week grandfather would get the nurses to bet on the horses for him and was often seen in his three wheeled bathtub armchair propelling himself to the nearest pub!

1935. Diana. Mum. and Eleanor outside Leys Farm. Attleborough.

Chapter 7

The Two World Wars

My father, Frank Peele, was born September 22nd 1900 and by the end of World War I was enlisted into the army. A photo of Father in uniform reminded me of other members of the family on my mother's side who fought in the 1914-1918 war. Father never saw active service as he failed on eyesight (having a left eye with little sight), flat feet and a bad back. In any case, the war was nearly over when he was called up. By the age of 19, Father had the responsibility of looking after Stanfield Hall Farm which then employed 12 men, while his father Ernest was taken to London to be weaned off alcohol. In his early years, Father rode a motor bike and often enjoyed escaping from the hard work and organising of the farm by taking trips out with his friend Mr Tiffin.

World War I canteen tent. (From postcard)

During World War I, old postcards sent by my mother's brothers, George and John Barnes, in 1915, show what life was like in the trenches. They were both accomplished horsemen and were lucky to survive the war. Robert Thomas Barnes or RT as the family called him, was their father and he farmed at the Hall, Long Stratton. My mother, Gertrude, was second from last of ten children and was born on December 13th 1900. She remembers her brothers going off to war and the anguish when all the best farm horses were taken for the same purpose. The local fire brigade was run from the Hall at Long Stratton and many a time the family were woken by the cries of 'fire!'. The engine was pulled by four horses, and it was these fit animals that were taken to pull the gun carriages and supplies during the war. At this time, 6d an hour was charged for the fire engine to be pumped.

R.T. Barnes and family at Long Stratton Hall
Left to right: R. T. Barnes, George Ling, Robert Charles, Ann Ling, John, Rosa Ling, Margaret (Peggy), Ethel, Elizabeth (Bubbles), Gertrude Janet, Flossie, Rosanna Barnes (née Baldwin).

Robert Thomas Barnes farmed several acres around Long Stratton and Wacton and was a horse dealer and slaughterer. He bought Hall Farm for £3500 and the Manor for £2500. The latter the government took over during the war. He married Rosanna Baldwin, one of a family of nine at Palgrave church in 1888. (The Barnes family tree can be found in the appendix).

Robert Barnes' brother-in-law; Robert Baldwin, was also in farming and a postcard dated 1905 was sent to R T Barnes regarding a delivery of a bullock. The postcard shows Robert Baldwin with his pony and trap in Diss, as this was the main mode of transport in the countryside at that time. In the early 1900s the post was delivered twice a day and long distance letters from Norwich to London went by train or plane. Sometimes these early double winged single engine planes had to make forced landings en route through lack of fuel. My husband has a faded photo dated 1912 of such an incident. He was told that the post plane from Norwich to London had to make a forced landing at Nazeing Common in Essex.

Before the war, it was man and horse power that produced the food for the country with every village having farms of differing sizes supporting different enterprises or a general covering of all types of stock and corn. The local men and boys were employed on the farms and this in turn created the community. Everyone knew their neighbours and helped each other at busy periods during the year. The local towns of Attleborough, Wymondham and Norwich were visited on market days and recreation took the form of sports like football, cricket, dances and the occasional silent film at the cinema.

Families were big in the late 19th century and early 20th century and my mother told me that her, and her brothers and sisters, known as 'the Barnes team', played cricket against the 'Greenwoods' who totalled nine in the family. In the early 1920s my mother and her sisters would go by pony and trap to dancing lessons at the Green Dragon in Wymondham. This is where she met my father, Frank Peele.

The seven Barnes sisters and friend Queenie on moat at Long Stratton Hall.

A postcard, kept tucked away in her writing box from her husband to be, says they could meet at the Green Dragon and he hoped it would be a bright moonlit night with a full moon. The Barnes' girls would load up in a horse gig and drive from Long Stratton to Wymondham wrapped in their long wool skirts, thick coats and hats and, guided by the flickering candle lights on the side of the gig and the stars above, make their way along the mud covered bumpy roads to Wymondham. There were no mobile telephones or heated cars like today. I like to think that youth then had a great pioneering spirit, but of course, it was the only way to get around. My parents married at Creeting St. Mary in Suffolk on June 4th 1924 where my mother was living with her brother John and sister Ethel.

They had moved to Eaton College farm at Creeting St. Mary after the death of their mother and the remarriage of their father, R. T. Barnes to Caroline Garrould, who was much younger. She soon spent the family wealth of farms on cars and furs etc. A few years later, Caroline and R. T.

56

Barnes retired to a cottage, penniless and with two more sons adding to the Barnes total. How fortunes can soon change!

June 4th 1924, wedding of Frank Peele to Gertrude Barnes.

During World War II, Frank Peele was farming at Rookery Farm, Thuxton, having moved there when Diana was six years old. My father joined the local fire brigade and was on duty at night after farming during the day. The old shed that was the fire brigade headquarters stood in the grounds of Ron Farrow's South Green Farm between Welborne and Mattishall and for many years was a reminder of the war and the local fire brigade.

My sister Diana, in her teens during the war, was a runner of messages. Her job was to bike down to the village, about a half mile away, to warn the residents of an impending invasion and to tell them to take cover. The only damage done to the Rookery Farm was on Sunday June 4th 1944 when an American plane from North Pickenham airfield, loaded with bombs, jettisoned some before crash landing on a pair of cottages near Garveston. Two bombs fell on the front meadow where the cows were grazing and injured one cow and cracked some of the windows in the front of the house. The worst thing about the accident was that the ten crew were all killed along with the two firemen who were putting out the blaze as the bombs exploded. Luckily, no one else was in the cottages that afternoon, which were completely destroyed. A family of evacuees who had escaped from the bombing in London, and thought they were safe in the countryside, were said to be living there at the time.

Wartime Fire Brigade at South Green Farm, Mattishall.

The Second World War took many able bodied young men from the farms. One was Bob Curson who had worked at Rookery Farm since leaving school in 1934. From 1939 he spent most of the war at Tek-el-Kebir near Cairo, as an engineer and tank inspector in the division known as the 'Desert Rats'. The son of a Welborne farmer, he was used to machinery and helped Father make one Fordson tractor out of two old worn out tractors. The 1939/41 rebuilt 'granny' Fordson is still around on the farm.

Left: Bob Curson at Tek-El-Kebir, nr. Cairo.
Right: Bob Curson and 'Basher' Bates with a Sherman tank.

Bob often mentions how, while cleaning out the turkey huts, then situated on rough ground in front of the house, (which later became a lawn and tennis court) he covered me with peat moss dust. Peat moss was then used as litter for poultry. I was just a baby in a pram and my mother was not very pleased to see what the wind and Bob had done to me. The pram and I were all covered in black dust! I was called *'Paddy the next best thing'* by an Irish nurse who delivered me in the Plantation Nursing home in Norwich. The nurse seemed to think that Thuxton, then a village of 26 houses, was a large place. My weight and size, under four pounds, in those days thought small for survival, caused a problem. No baby clothes fitted and I was, according to Mother, first wrapped in cotton wool and a doll's dress.

Coming into this world 12 years and 9 months after my sister, Diana, with no siblings between us, it was quite a shock for my parents, as I was not planned and my mother found out only two months before I arrived that she was expecting. Naturally my parents had hoped for a pigeon pair

59

and I would be a boy, especially as it was presumed I would arrive in March. Mother was chased by a bull on April 1st and felt sure I would be an April Fool, but I finally made an entrance 16 days later - not the son my parents had hoped for!

Father decided I would be christened Patricia, a proper girl's name. As a child he called me Paddy, but altered to Pat as soon as I left school and took an interest in farming. He said Pat was short for Patrick, the boy's name I would have been called if I had been a son. Many years later when I was in my twenties and walking from Norwich Market, arm in arm with Father, we met an old friend of Father's who did not know of my existence and accused him of having a *'young piece on the side'*. Father saw the funny side of the situation! In the Barnes' family circles I was one of the 'late hatch' having three other cousins nearer my age, the rest of my cousins being old enough to have children of their own. This often occurred in large families in the late 19th and early 20th centuries when children would be at school alongside the next generation of the family.

My memories of the Second World War are sketchy. Only one night really stands out in my memory, when Norwich was getting bombed in April 1942. Mother hurried me out of the house and we hid in one of the grassy hollows on the front meadow. Many years later I found out that this hollow was the main street between the houses of the 'lost medieval village of Thuxton'. But on that fateful night the sky was full of streaks of light. Searchlights seemed to beam from all directions and a glow could be seen in the distance towards Norwich. Mother was always attracted to lightning and thunderstorms. I think she thought the idea of these pretty patterns playing in the sky would interest my childish mind, as I could not sleep. There were several bangs and thuds of bombs going off which shook the ground and doodle bugs whining overhead. They seemed to chug their way towards Norwich. The time to worry was if the motor cut out for they could turn and come back on themselves.

Fortunately for us this did not happen. But the devastation to some of the well known shops in Norwich was catastrophic. Curls store, where Debenhams now stands, was flattened and for many years was an eyesore to the city with a deep hole and brick rubble where the store used to be. Each year purple rose bay willow herb and yellow ragwort flowered among the devastation. Mother had bought two Wilton carpets from the shop just a few weeks before the air raid. The carpet department asked if she would sell them back so they had stock to start with when the shop was rebuilt. The carpets never moved back to Norwich and the blue decorative patterned carpet that graced my parents' bedroom lasted all their life with the brown Wilton with its green border gracing the spare bedroom well into the 21st century.

On the night of the raid on Norwich, Father was on fire service duty and my sister Diana had gone down to the village on her bike as a messenger to warn of the attacks. On returning indoors, a bomb blast had not affected the structure of the house, but the geraniums, that Mother cherished, were sitting quite upright on the bathroom windowsill, with the saucers, they once sat on, all smashed on the floor! The mending basket with pins, reels of sylko cotton and cards of wool for repairing socks were immersed in a pool of sewing machine oil, all of which had leapt from the book shelf in the living room. These little things that exasperated Mother seemed to have left an impression on my young mind. The old wireless, with its accumulators that had to go away to be recharged, was regularly listened to for news of other possible raids. Eventually in 1945 we heard the news of victory. A celebration party was held at Garveston Village Hall. I remember loading up on a decorated cart pulled by an equally decorated horse and jogging the two miles from Rookery Farm, Thuxton, collecting other children from the village on the way.

It was an era of make do and mend. The string and brown paper that wrapped parcels was carefully untied and kept for another time. Nothing was wasted, especially not food. Once a week during harvest, there was a delivery of agricultural pies, nicknamed 'the Woolton pie' after the then Minister of Food, Lord Woolton. They were made by the Women's Voluntary Service (WVS) and contained various vegetables in pastry. These came by train to Thuxton Station and were for the men and women that worked on the farm. Mother was always dubious about eating them for fear they contained cat or dog meat!

We were fortunate living on the farm as it meant we had fresh eggs, poultry, milk and pork after a pig was killed and stored away in the cellar. This helped with the food rationing permits. Bees were added to the farm when it was announced that extra rations of sugar would be given to bee keepers to feed the bees through the hard winters. Naturally some of the sugar made it into the house for cooking and preserving. Butter was made from the milk and wild rabbits made a succulent pie. Vegetables were grown in the garden and blackberries and fruit were gathered from the hedgerows. Sticks and wood collected created the warmth, and a fire for cooking, with a lump or two of slag coal. This coal was not the best but was allowed for farmers to use when threshing the corn or ploughing with giant steam engines and cable ploughs. The War Agricultural Committee used these puffing monsters to turn areas of grassland into food production. An engine placed at one end of a large field would gently wind a strong steel cable, across a stretch of land to another quietly puffing steam engine the other side. Attached to this cable was a large piece of metal in the form of a plough. This means of ploughing turned many commons and heath land, once used for recreation and shooting, into acres of corn to feed the people during the war. Young girls from towns and villages volunteered to work on the land, sometimes using these machines. Bill Abel's sister Maud, was a tall strong girl who joined the Women's Land Army. After the war she helped my mother in the house, often turning up on her bike dressed in the khaki bib and brace overall and coat issued as Land Army dress.

After the war farmers were encouraged to use fertilizer and were paid grants to drain land and remove hedges to enable them to produce more food. Rationing of food through a system of coupons was introduced in 1940 and carried on until 1954. It was during the early 1950s that fresh tropical fruit like oranges and grapefruit were once again imported into the country. Mother planted some pips from the first grapefruit she ate after the war. The pips grew in a pot on the kitchen windowsill and the one strong surviving seedling was transferred to a bigger container in the spare bedroom. With the care and attention that was always given to all the plants, the grapefruit became too big for the room and it was time to keep or despatch it.

A conservatory was built on the south wall near the house by Herbert Clarke of Weston Longville and the grapefruit plant was dug into the ground in the corner of this new construction. In 1962, 12 years after the pip was sown, the young tree produced its first crop of 12 yellow grapefruit. They each weighed between 12oz. to 1lb and were duly displayed in a basket and photographed. The skin was rather thick because of the lack of warm sunshine but the fruit inside was delicious, with a slightly tart taste. The unusual thing is that the fruit has never had any pips inside to reproduce any more grapefruit. The tree is still going strong and has had a sprinkle of sweet smelling flowers each spring while supporting ripening fruit from the previous years' flowers. Now, after 60 years the conservatory is worn and the tree has escaped its branches to the fresh air outside the broken glass top. It has been cut back several times, suffered smutty leaves and attacks of scale and insects. Old friends and locals still ask about my mother's pride and joy. It was thought to be the first grapefruit tree reared from a pip after the war, to produce fruit in Norfolk.

Mother displaying fruit on her home grown grapefruit tree. (Photograph courtesy of EDP)

63

Chapter 8

Diana's Memories

The following chapter is taken directly from notes my sister Diana made about her early life on the farm.

Old converted Morris car and free range turkeys.

'Poultry were the life line for my parents when we moved to Rookery Farm, Thuxton from Downham Grove near Wymondham in 1932 when I was six years old. The farm was all grass and in a very bad state. Dad kept the free range hens he brought from Wymondham, in a red single decker bus in the paddock and a bus on the rough back meadow. The old red single decker buses acted as shelter and a place to lay their eggs. There was one bus up the yard by the cow house that Dad cleaned and packed the eggs in. I remember, when I was older, standing on a stool, washing the dirty eggs, as they were all free range and dirty and putting them on a wire netting frame to drain. They all had to be graded, by hand, one at a time, on a small container for large, standard and small and packed in

64

boxes. Later Dad bought three large huts which were kept on the meadow in front of Abbot's where several hens were kept free range. Dad had an old Morris car. He put a wooden frame on the back with an old water tank on and would carry the water and food by car to feed and water the hens, collecting the eggs in pails to bring up to wash and grade. I remember going round various houses delivering eggs to householders. If I was lucky and was a good girl, I got halfpence of aniseed balls or an ice cream. All luxuries in those days.

Bob Curson joined Father when he left school to help on the farm in 1934. Dad had horses at that time, and Charlie Page would plough and do the work on the farm with them. In 1941, Dad bought two old Fordson tractors and made a working one from them. Gradually the horses went and the tractor took over.

At age of ten I had moved to Dereham Secondary School. I would bike down to Thuxton Station and leave my bike there, catch the train to Dereham where we then had to walk quite a way to school, all weathers. I enjoyed my days at school but I hated the Maths and History teachers. You were not allowed to make a noise! I loved Domestic Science when we learnt to cook and launder. I also took Music lessons at dinner hour. All the school pupils had to attend Assembly in the big hall each morning, and I had to take my turn in playing the piano for pupils to march in. Miss Galloway, the Head Teacher, would attend with prayer and announcements. Then I would play for them to march out. Lessons would then begin. We all had our own classrooms and sat at desks where our books etc. would be kept and the teachers of various subjects would come to us. I was not a bright scholar but in the last year I was made a Prefect which I was very proud of and also won the music prize. I could have gone to Harper Adams Poultry College but I didn't want to and instead I worked at home helping Mother in the house, feeding the hens and turkeys and assisting Dad in making bigger huts round the outside of the paddock. These had wire mesh frames in front of the hut for the young turkeys to go into during the day, but all had to be shut in at night in case a rat got in and killed them.

Hedgehogs were a great nuisance and got into the hens nest boxes and sucked the yolk out of the eggs. It made Dad and me so angry. When I was old enough, I would take my dog and a firm stick and kill them. It is said a hedgehog can eat a whole hen sitting on a nest, therefore I hate hedgehogs. I was not very keen helping with the cows and calves but did have to help with the mucking out etc.

Saturday was a great day when Mum and Dad and I would visit the Norwich Cattle Market to see cattle sold and we would have our lunch up there. Sometimes a calf would be tied in a sack with its head sticking out and taken on the back seat of the car to be sold at Norwich Market. In the months after Christmas we would drive into Norwich and go to the pictures and then have our tea at Buntings restaurant, which was a large store like Debenhams. Mum and I also visited Woolworths each week where everything was sold for sixpence. That is how Mother collected her china tea service, buying one cup or saucer per week.

Norwich Market in the early 1900s.

As regards the arable land, Dad would see to the ploughing and drilling

66

etc. and during the years he hired five charity fields up the road towards Mattishall which were not very large and needed a lot to put them right. At harvest time Dad bought a binder which went behind the tractor to cut the corn and bundle it into sheaves which were then thrown out the back. These then had to be stood up in shocks (Norfolk term for stooks), six or eight sheaves to a shock to ripen off and keep the wet out. This was one of my jobs all day, very often with Maud, Bill Abel's sister. Bill was relief cowman then. When it came to carting it up to the stack yard I had the job of standing on the wagon or driving the tractor shock to shock. The sheaves were made into large stacks going to a point at the top with eaves and had to be thatched to keep the wet out.

Father driving Allis Chalmers tractor and Bob Curson on Albion binder.

Dad did quite a lot of contract work, binder cutting for neighbours to earn extra money. In late autumn or early in the year the steam threshing engine and drum along with men that travelled with it would come to the stack yard to thresh the corn out. What a dirty job that was. Near the bottom of the stack rats would run everywhere. I, my dog and stick would chase and kill them. In the afternoons at 3pm, Mum always made a cup of

67

tea, when the men would come up to the door to drink, or if Dad or Bob were working in the field, I would have to take a bottle of tea to them.

Of course, I had to bike everywhere. On Friday evenings it was Dereham Young Farmers Club meeting night which I joined, biking there with Billy Abel. This is where I learnt a lot and was soon made secretary, and gained confidence as I arranged speakers, quizzes, debates etc. There was a small musical group of us who would go round entertaining. I played the piano and sang. Norfolk had a good Young Farmer's Club leader, Gordon Moseley, who in 1950 arranged a week's visit to the Channel Isles and my friend Betty Ewin persuaded Dad and Mum to let us go and, of course, I met up with Peter who became my husband.

Mother and Diana finishing stumping turkeys.
(Photograph courtesy of EDP)

I never had much to do with the cows and calves until 31ˢᵗ January 1947 when it snowed very heavily and roads got completely blocked. Dad said to me, 'you've got to learn to milk this morning'. So, as it was still milking by hand, sitting on a stool, it was very slow going with 22 cows to milk.

I didn't like the cows that kicked. There were floods everywhere when the snow melted in March and near Thuxton Station it was all flooded. Not long after this Dad had Alfa Laval milking machines installed.

It was a busy time feeding the turkeys in the autumn to get ready for the Christmas trade. We would start plucking about December 9th, when the barn would have all been cleaned up and clean straw spread all over the floor to catch any blood and stray feathers.

*Father and Charlie Page grading rough plucked
turkeys to hang in the barn at Rookery Farm.
(Photograph courtesy of EDP)*

A lot of labour was needed as turkeys had to be caught up in a trailer from sheds and brought to the barn where they were carried up the stairs, across the aisle to be shut in a dark room at the top of the barn and about

69

10 – 15 men would come to earn some extra money. By day men would come in and catch them one by one and kill, pluck and stump them. Dad devised a chute.

1953, evening drinks.
Left to right, Paddy, Peter Howlett, Bob Curson, Bill Abel and Walter Bowers.

Mum who was in charge of the stumping bay, would lift a lid and the finished turkey would slide down to Dad below in the barn. Here he would weigh each one and tie a weight label round the neck and a piece of string round its feet to hang it up on hangs in appropriate weights. Cutting binder twine string into lengths for tying the feet and cutting white string to thread the labels was another job for me. This would take several evenings before plucking began. I would help Mother stump the turkeys, make coffee in the morning, tea in the afternoon, then prepare sandwiches and cake for tea for whoever was there.

About 8pm I would then have to give them a drink of ale. I then would help Dad to sort out orders or answer the phone. I did not like the dressing which my mother was in charge of. For these orders the turkeys were

70

carried up the stairs again to be stripped of the remaining feathers and then dressed.

1953, left to right; Mother, Diana, Maud Abel, and Paddy.

In the end I did sort out a few giblets and put them with the dressed turkeys which were then carried down to the bottom of the barn where Dad weighed the final dressed bird, priced and booked it before putting it on a shelf. The weather was so much cooler with sharp frosts in those days which helped, as all the turkeys were stored in the barn and one adjoining shed. Time would come when turkeys to be sent away would have to be packed in a box and labelled 'ready for collection' to go to London or various parts of the country. The busy time would finally come to an end when people came to collect their turkey from the farm. Then there would be the job to find where you had put them. The time soon passed and I always enjoyed every minute of it although it was very tiring. Father's training stood me in good stead to look after the customer and be very polite'.

*Charlie Page, Father and Diana grading and wrapping
oven ready turkeys for transport.
(Photograph courtesy of EDP)*

Chapter 9

After the War

During and after the Second World War farmers found their produce was needed. Rabbits and poultry in the country were not subject to the tight food rationing and were prized items, making good money. Mother hatched turkeys under broody hens on the lawn at Thuxton during the 1930s depression, until I arrived in 1939. Father then took over the hatching and soon found a way of producing more chicks without the need of broody hens. He invested in Gloucester and Glevam incubators which held 100 to 150 eggs each and were heated by paraffin oil. The eggs were marked with an 'X' on one side and an 'O' on the other and turned by hand morning and night.

Gloucester incubator with eggs on tray.
(Photograph, 'Modern Poultry Keeping)

The incubators were situated in various sheds near the house until a proper incubator shed attached to the house, was built in 1945. That incubator shed is still in use today. The first job for this new shed was Diana's 21st birthday party and with a smooth concrete floor, it made an ideal dance floor! Father made me sit on a sack and I was pulled around to help polish the surface of the floor with 'french chalk', a substance that made the floor highly polished and suitable for dancing. Being about six years old at the time, I do not know what went on in the evening, but in later life have heard of the various tales from ex-Dereham Young Farmers about cars hitting barrels of a substance called milky whey and leaving the farm rather stickier and fouler smelling than when they arrived!

After the party, held in July, Mother got the local beekeeper to take the honey off for extracting and suggested the frames could be stored in the incubator shed ready for spinning out and potting up. The bees had another idea and the next day the shed was full of angry furry creatures taking the honey back to their hives. The decorations were laden with bees trying to escape with their bounty and the noise was incredible. The bees had found the air cowling in the ceiling and once in had a job to find their way out.

A few years later, Number 7, an ex-army hut from Shipdham was obtained and put in the orchard part of the garden for more Gloucester and Glevam incubators. These were situated at one end and the chick brooders the other end. I think the brooders were designed by my father and were heated by paraffin, having a dark warm area where the chicks could sleep and a light area for them to feed and water. A Norwich firm, Cope and Cope made these brooders and they were used until quite recently giving the best results. The chicks for the first three weeks are off the ground, away from draughts and predators like rats and cats and can rest in the dark like under a mother hen. They come out to get food and water when their bodies require refreshment. Modern brooders do not allow the chicks to get away from the heat and light and therefore are brought up in a 'stressed' situation from the start.

George Barnes (Mum's brother) of Old Hall Farm, Fritton, a farmer and slaughterer by trade, had helped my parents with bronze poults when they moved to Thuxton. Uncle George, as we knew him, was a well known person in the area. He wore a wide brimmed trilby hat, with holes made in the sides over his receding ginger hair. He once told me that the holes were for '*letting the steam out*'. It was during the 1960s that once a week George would phone my father to have a chat about life in general and what was happening on the farm. He often complained about the supersonic bangs that the new jet aeroplanes and later the Concord made when going through the sound barrier. He felt sure that this juddering affected the hatchability of the eggs and had a novel idea of putting each leg of his Gloucester incubators in old worn out rubber boots to stop the movement.

George Barnes (plus hat) and free range turkeys.
(Photograph courtesy of EDP)

One night he was so busy doing his weekly talk on the phone to my parents, that he forgot to put the trays of eggs back into the incubators and they were left out all night. I'll bet the steam did rise inside his trilby when he found what he had done! He need not have worried though, as a few days later he had an excellent hatch. It was usual to copy what the mother hen would do a few days before hatching and leave the eggs out of the incubator to cool. The hen leaves the nest for several hours to feed and stretch her legs before sitting tight while the eggs hatch. The eggs get cold. This allows the pores in the frail warm shell to cool and take in oxygen in the air sack of the egg, so helping the chick in the next two days with oxygen and energy to break out of the shell.

Small homemade rearing huts with white turkeys in sun parlour.
(Photograph, 'Modern Poultry Keeping')

The small wooden huts that Diana referred to, that were made in the 1940s, were constructed from the wooden crating that the Model T Ford cars came in from America. Father also bought wood from Wenns of Yarmouth. In later years, when we had our holidays at Gorleston, Father would love to motor past the quay and smell the wood piled high at Wenns. The small huts he built are still occasionally used, but have become fragile after being moved from their original resting place. They were made to rear about 50 chicks under a round paraffin heater which had felt or sacking covering it that acted as a curtain for the chicks to hide under in the dark and warm, just like under a hen. A wood and wire netting construction called a sun parlour was attached to each hut so that when the chicks were old enough, they could go out into the sun and fresh air. This allowed them to get feathered before going into bigger sheds or out into the field.

Before the Second World War, Dick and Cath Gowing, cousins on the Barnes side of the family, would spend their holidays at the farm with Diana and loved to ride in the old Morris car which was converted for carrying pails of corn and eggs to and from the turkeys and hens. This was the car my sister later learnt to drive. As she was the right age to drive when the war broke out, she never had to take a driving test. My mother, who started driving after the war to take me to Lyndhurst School in Wymondham, had to take lessons and pass a test. Diana remembers her first driving experience on the farm taking grandfather Ernest Peele in the old Morris car to the harvest field. Instead of keeping to the roadways and driving around the shocks, she ran over the top of them, getting stuck on top of a shock. A few strong words were said by Father!

Left to right, Dick Gowing and Diana with Cath Gowing and Father, on an old Morris car ready to feed turkeys.

My first recollection of the farmhouse kitchen at Rookery Farm was of a big copper set in the corner of the kitchen belching steam on a Monday washday. A long wooden stick and pair of wood tongs all bleached white from the boiling water, sat on the side. The copper was set on a stone wall and had a wooden lid, with a fire place underneath that was used to heat the water that had been drawn from the well. Father had a little engine housed in a small green shed in the back yard near the well, which pumped the water into a tank above the dairy. This was quite an improvement from some homes that had to pull the water by hand from the well. Rain water was collected from the roof of the house and surrounding sheds in galvanised water tanks. This soft water, as it was called, was heated in a kettle over the old cooking range for washing our hair. Mother insisted it was kinder to the face as well as to the hair. There were no extravagant shampoos in those days and hair rinsed with a touch of vinegar gave a lovely sheen. The older ladies would also rinse their hair in water with a touch of 'blue bag'. The blue bag helped to tint the white hair of ladies who were turning grey. Mother was a great advocate of using Reckitt and Colman blue bag products to give white cotton sheets and table cloths a clean blue look when used with Robinson's starch. Each Monday the sheets, pillow cases, table cloths, napkins and anything else that needed a bit of stiffening and whitening were treated, followed by a sprinkling of water if they were too dry to iron and rolled tight, ready for a Tuesday session of smoothing and completing the stiffening with a hot iron.

When I was a child, bath time was once a week and taken in an old enamel bath housed downstairs in a room next to the kitchen. As there was no running water over the bath, the water had to be heated via the copper fired by sticks and coal and carried to the bath in jugs or a pail. I suppose the enamel bath was a step up from the tin bath that some people owned. At least our enamel bath had a plug and an outlet to a drain outside. My sister and cousin Cath remember Father having fun by producing the yard broom and pretending to scrub them down. I can imagine the screams! The toilet was outside across the back yard from the kitchen in a range of low buildings that comprised sheds used for wood and coal. A grand mahogany seat with the required hole covered a large pail and many black looking spiders. I hated going by torchlight or candle to do

78

the necessary before going to bed. Otherwise it was using the chamber pot, which was just another job to empty the following morning for my very busy mother. When the men on the farm emptied the toilet bucket outside, I was not allowed to be around. In towns, the 'soil cart' round would be done at night when people were out of the way. Quite a smelly job I imagine, but for country properties, a boon for the garden, especially the rhubarb. Father had his own toilet at the back of the granary. This also doubled up as a toilet for the men who worked on the farm. Later in the 1940s a flush toilet was put into the men's department and a bathroom made upstairs in one of the bedrooms, with all mod cons plus running hot water. What a relief not to go out in the rain and dark as a late night event!

I never really experienced candle power, as we had a 110 watt generator engine that provided light and pumped water for the house. Later in the 1950s when things became more mechanised, a Ruston Hornby engine was put in one of the sheds opposite the house with a large metal water cooling tank on a concrete base built outside the shed. The Ruston Hornby engine would be started early each morning with a cartridge that banged the engine into life and shook me out of my dreams! My bedroom overlooked the engine shed. Power was then provided for lights in the house and a vacuum cleaner, washing machine and an electric iron. Much improved on the old box iron so called where a brick was heated in the fire and put hot into a metal box with its handle and smooth bottom surface to iron the cloths. In 1952, the engine supplied heat to run the small Weston electric incubator that Father invested in to hatch the turkeys, so doing away with the daily chore of filling paraffin lamps that heated the Gloucester and Glevam incubators and the twice daily turning of the eggs by hand.

Snippets of what now seems such an idyllic childhood, come to mind as I remember the 1940s. The six men on the farm helping Father, all coming from local villages by bicycle or walking, looked out for me as I played around the farm. What a fright I gave them when at the age of about seven, I decided to give the cats on the farm a party. Part of a tree was taken up the steps of the old granary and old Victorian Christmas candles set in metal clips were attached to the tree. Just like the tree would be decorated for Christmas Day. Food was laid out and various cats ranging from black and white, tabby and my favourite tortoiseshell cat were taken up the granary. Then I lit the candles. With the late afternoon light fading, the effect, from the distance through the top window of the granary, made the building look as if it was on fire. Charlie and Father, red faced and out of breath, appeared and my innocent game was soon extinguished. I knew all the cats on the farm and had a family tree, but when the number got to 20, Father took action while I was away at school and that ended my primitive form of bookkeeping. I have always had cats and only last year I had a letter addressed to the *'cat lady'*. The sender had forgotten my name but knew the address as she had picked up some kittens earlier in the year. I suppose the liking of cats came from my grandmother Eleanor, who I am told, in the 1920s would take her black cat on a lead for walks when she was on holiday at Gorleston.

*1927, Gorleston Pier. Mother and Dorothy
Baxter with Diana in pram.*

80

During January and February the hedges and ditches were cut back and cleaned out by spade by the men on the farm. The gaps in the thorn hedges were made good by cutting a large thorn branch almost through the bottom of the stem and bending it down across the gap and weaving other stems through. When spring came, the thorn would spring into life and soon close the gap. Thorn hedges were put in over 200 years ago when the commons were enclosed. Small birds such as hedge sparrows, thrush, blackbird, yellowhammer and finches would use these tight hedges as nesting places away from the prying eyes of magpies, jays and hawks. All of whom either take the eggs or kill the small birds. With the mechanical cutting of these old hedges, the reduction in hiding places and food in the form of berries has been a contributing factor to the decreasing population of small birds. The use of DDT to control insects has also not helped.

I think of my childhood days when I would go around the hedges and note where the thrush or blackbird was nesting. I marvelled at the mud lined nest of the song thrush with its tiny brown spots on the pale blue eggs. I remember the delight in finding a yellowhammer's nest and took one of the fragile eggs for my collection. In those days it was not illegal to take birds' eggs for a collection and I had an egg of most common species. Charlie Page taught me how to blow the yolk out so that the egg could be preserved and I proudly had them displayed in old tins on cotton wool. I was lucky to see a nest with a rather large egg nestled amongst the smaller speckled hedge sparrows eggs. A few days later I found one large greedy fledgling being fed by harassed parents and realised it was a young cuckoo. What a big wide open mouth it had. No wonder the foster parents were constantly feeding their baby.

As a child, the front meadow near the house had all sorts of flowers and in the spring I would gather arms full of cowslips and primroses to take home to Mother. It was only when more grass was needed for the expanding dairy herd that fertilizer and sprays were used to make the grass grow quicker and weed free. The grass then got grazed closer to the ground and the fragile flowers ceased to come each year in the meadow. Thankfully they can still be found on the sides of banks and ditches. The old original 'Lent Lily' seems to be another casualty of the modern world. With its yellow trumpet and fragile light yellow petals, it could be found in many undisturbed pastures where animals and men had not compacted the soil. The farm where I now live is called 'Lent Farm' and was rebuilt after a fire in the season of Lent, so I was informed by the previous owners. The Derisleys had always kept the lawn tidy by using a scythe with no compaction to the grass. Lent lilies came up all over the lawn. But from 1965 we used a Suffolk Punch mower with a roller and cutter to give the grass a well manicured look. Sadly, within three years we had lost the lilies with only an occasional leaf appearing in the spring. I think of Wordsworth poem of 'Daffodils' and realise in some cases how fragile nature is when set against our human race.

Chapter 10

Weather Extremes and The Beccles Cattle Show

The weather is often the subject of conversation and can be the first line of contact with complete strangers. The friendly postman who delivers the letters each morning has always a remark about the heat or wet day to come. Many parts of the country have their own sayings but one I remember would always be uttered by Bill the cowman when the sun was shining, 'Phoebe's out'. Many of the older generation remember the hot summer in 1946 when the village ponds that watered cattle, sheep and horses went dry and the surface wells stopped producing water. Mains water did not exist in some parts of the countryside, it was only the natural springs that provided water for people to collect in containers and use sparingly.

We were lucky at Thuxton as the well for the farm was deep. Father had converted the pumping of water from a broken Victorian windmill pump to a more modern petrol driven one. This supplied water to a 1000 gallon tank in the top of the barn which in turn graduated the water to tanks at the bottom of the front meadow and horse meadow. During the war, the beaches had been mined, so there were no seaside visits until the 1950s. It had been so hot one evening in 1946, that Father, Mother, Diana and I walked in our swimming costumes down to the bottom of the front meadow and got into the old half ships cast iron boiler that acted as a water tank. Being rather on the small side, I had a job to stand up as the water was up to my mouth. What a wet sight we must have looked that late evening picking our way back through the tussocks of dry grass and dried up thistles! I learnt to swim at Lyndhurst School when we were taken for swimming classes to a pool in Wymondham somewhere on Queen Street. With the help of a belt supporting my body, the instructor would bark out instructions while dangling me on a pole like a fishing rod. To this day my confidence in the water has never been very good. Sometimes the family would go to see Auntie Ann Gowing at Riverside, Costessey, where Diana and our cousins Cath, Dick and Gwen Gowing would swim across the river. A frightening experience for some, as the water ran fast because there was a sluice further down the river.

1949, Lyndhurst school. Paddy in back row, second from left.

The hot summer of 1946 was followed by one of the worst winters for generations. It started to snow January 31st 1947 and did not melt enough for us to leave the farm until March 11th. The snow blew under the tiles of the farmhouse and when the thaw came, water dripped through the ceilings everywhere. The landing became a battlefield of bowls and pails that had to be negotiated and then the ceiling in the box room fell down. This was the only time my sister had to milk the cows by hand. She did not like them and preferred working with Mother and the poultry. Billy Abel, the cowman, who normally came to work on a motorbike, was marooned at home two miles away in Garvestone. The only way to get to the farm was by walking across the fields and as Billy was disabled with a bad leg, this was very difficult in the snow. His sister Maud was a tall strong girl and had seen service in the Women's Land Army before helping my mother in the house. Maud walked with Billy across the fields known then as the Grove and helped him over ditches and snowdrifts to the farm.

Mother made up the old feather mattress and bed and gave him some of Father's dry clothes and he stayed with us all winter to help milk the cows. The milk was made into butter and I expect the pigs fattened on the rest when the lorry did not get to the farm to collect. At one time the baker got down to the farm from Mattishall and not being able to get to the village at Thuxton, Diana and Mother put the bread into washed hessian bran sacks and set off to the village ¾ mile away. They left me behind for fear of me getting lost in a drift. I was most upset. The only semi solid thing to walk on was the hedge as the road had filled to ten feet deep. In our yard to me it was like being in the Arctic, with a passage cut from the cowshed to the house. The men bound my legs and the top of my boots with old sacking to keep the snow out, just like they wore normally when working around the farm. For three months I missed school and hated going back in May to catch up on my spelling, something that still bothers me today.

The winters used to have frosts regularly, hard enough to freeze the broads and part of the fens for ice-skating. In 1963 it just kept on freezing. It started on Boxing Day 1962 and continued well into March 1963. By the 1960s, most homes had mains water and sanitation. The continuing frost froze the pipes underground to a depth of two feet and in some parts of the country where metal pipes had been used to convey water, the only way to keep the pipes running free with water was to put an electric current through the pipe. At Thuxton, as there was no mains water to supply the farm, we had to attach a plastic pipe to the outlet of the deep bore pump and let the pipe fill the water tank in the house and cattle drinking tanks in the yard, before quickly rolling the pipe up and storing it overnight in the cowshed. This was the warmest place on the farm. Even the cats knew where to keep warm when the weather was bad and would sneak into the cowshed for a lap of warm milk and then curl up near a cow for warmth. Billy always gave the cats some dry bread soaked in the milk washings in an old baking tin.

1963, winter at Rookery Farm.
Yard with Dutch barn for storing hay and straw

The summer of 1947 saw the introduction of Alfa Laval bucket milking machines and an increase in cows. Father went over to keeping Friesians when so many of his old favourite cows were slaughtered because they had TB. He bought a young Friesian bull from his brother-in-law, Charles Barnes at Mill Farm, Tharston which was turned out with a group of young female heifers on the front meadow. This bull had not got the docile character of his predecessor, the Red Poll bull, and soon became quite aggressive. After attacking the cowman, he was soon got rid of. It was about this time that artificial insemination (A.I.) was started and Father took advantage of this service. Bulls of different breeds were kept around the country at various centres where the semen was collected and taken frozen in a flask to the farm when required. In Norfolk, the main centre for holding the bulls was at Beccles with a sub-centre for semen at Wymondham. A phone call made early in the morning that a cow was 'on heat', would mean that an inseminator was out to the farm by midday with semen from the bull of your choice. This allowed the farmer to improve the type of animals for dairy or beef production and avoided having dangerous bulls around the farm.

Bill showing cow at Beccles A.I. show.

In the 1950s a show was held at Beccles centre where farmers could take the progeny of these bulls and compete at show standard. This was judged on breed type according to age group etc. I was quite enthusiastic at this showing lark and helped Billy at weekends and holidays to wash and groom the two animals that we thought were suitable. The fun came when training them to lead and many times I saw Billy being dragged along the roadway. The cows in those days had horns which we polished to make them shine. I thought that my cow Jane would look pretty with her curved horns painted with clear nail varnish. The judge at the show was not impressed! Nor were the other cows on the farm. Jane would go back to the field after her wash and walk and bellow loudly about her treatment. One day the other cows thought Jane was getting too much attention and knocked her into the water tank. That soon put her in her place. I always enjoyed the Beccles show as Father would take me out of school for the day. Nowadays, with the increase of numbers of cows in a herd, often over 200 in a group in one shed, it has been essential to de-horn the progeny as calves, to stop the horns from growing. Some breeds like the Red Poll are naturally polled and do not have horns. Fighting and damage by horns can be a dairy farmer's nightmare but a vet's profitable heaven!

Paddy and cousin, Doreen Pearson (née Winter), training cows for show.

Chapter 11

Turkey Times

Memo. from . . .

Phone—Mattishall 237
Telegrams—Peele, Thuxton, Norfolk
Station—Thuxton, L.N.E.R. ¼ mile

F. E. PEELE
Farmer and Poulterer

THUXTON, NORFOLK
NEW LAID EGGS
Home Dressed Poultry

BREEDER OF MAMMOTH BRONZE AND NORFOLK BLACK TURKEYS
Member of Mammoth Bronze and Norfolk Black Turkey Clubs. S.P.B.A. and P.C.

CHRISTMAS ORDERS

Dear Sir or Madam,

    It is with pleasure that I solicit the favour of your Christmas order again this year, and it is most essential owing to National Emergency conditions that I hope to receive your requirements VERY EARLY.

    With war conditions now existing, and the Rationing Scheme ~~which will be enforced in the very near future~~, I am glad to inform all my customers despite the food regulations that TURKEYS AND POULTRY are exempt from the scheme. It will therefore be possible for customers to select their own choice of weight bird as in past years, from the very fine Flock of Turkeys now being fattened at my own Farm.

    All birds are reared and fed on the best homegrown foods, and their weights range from 7 lbs. to 30 lbs., and every one is guaranteed to be Prime Norfolk.

    There have been no Shows arranged for 1939, but I had the pleasure and distinct honour of winning at the 1938 Olympia Show, two Cups, one being for the best table type of bird in the Show, which speaks for itself.

    Chickens, Ducks or Geese also, of all weights can be supplied at the keenest market prices.

    Thanking you for past favours and assuring you of our best service.

Yours faithfully,

F. E. PEELE.

Christmas turkey orders, wartime letter.

Turkeys and the poultry side of the farm never really interested me when I was young. I found my parents and my sister were always discussing turkeys. What should be done for Christmas or what medication should be given for a group of turkeys with coccidiosis or liver complaint. It seemed to me, as a child, that Father would call the vet for the slightest

89

illness a turkey had, but ignore a cow down with milk fever. Now I am older and looking back, I can see why the efforts and work were put into the poultry side of the farm. Turkeys were a profitable delicacy and only eaten at Christmas. They were not subject to the strict food rationing of other meats and by the 1950s were gaining in recognition as producing meat that was good value for money.

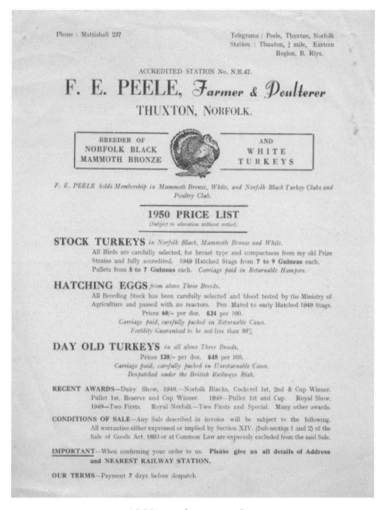

1950s, turkey price list.

Before the war, Father bought in Mammoth Bronze turkeys to make up the number of birds sent to the London Market. Around 1,600 rough plucked turkeys were packed onto a large Easton Roadways chain driven lorry and trailer for Smithfield and the London markets. Each bird had a clip attached to the wing called a 'National Mark', with a label around the neck stating the producer's name and weight of the bird in pounds.

My first memories of the turkeys was as a child, going out with Mother on a moonlit night as it became dusk, putting the turkeys up on poles attached to iron hurdles. These black vulture like creatures looked an eerie sight sitting on these makeshift perches in the middle of a large meadow, with the brown owl making its customary screeching noise.

Hurdles as perches for free range turkeys.

If given the chance, the original breeds of turkeys like to roost away from ground predators and will go up trees or sit on sheds if the wing feathers are not clipped. The structure of the modern white bred turkey is too heavy and clumsy to do what its ancestors once did. The turkey field or bush meadow was wired in with netting about six feet high. This kept the turkeys within the field but free range. Nearer to Christmas it was a constant job for Father or Bob to take it in turns to patrol the area at night with a gun to shoot the foxes that would pick up the birds not gone to roost on the hurdles. Female turkeys can fly a short distance, but the males, being heavier, hardly leave the ground. Sometimes the turkeys would find a hole in the wire netting and escape into neighbour Claude Banham's rough ground. This area was once the site of the old village of Thuxton, occupied until the 17th century. Two hundred years later it became an imprint and memory of past history, with its hollows and humps in the ground, oak trees, brambles and rough grass. This area gave ideal treats for turkeys who, like pheasants, are quite happy eating acorns, blackberries, hawthorn, corn and seeds. It was a nightmare to round them up from this jungle, as a turkey when frightened will go into a hedge or bramble bush head first and just keep going further in. They do not seem to have the sense to back out and will stay head first in the bush until they die.

MANAGEMENT COMMITTEE MEET, BUT THIS TIME FOR COCKTAILS

An informal gathering in the Chairman's suite last night included many of the Management Committee. A brief report of this meeting by the Chairman of the publicity committee appears beneath this picture. L. to R.: B. Matthews, M. Bradley, J. Goddard, Dr. W. McKay, J. Cassidy, R. Moston, Mrs. MacKenzie, L. Western, T. Duke, F. Peele, G. Llewellin, A. H. Johnson, F. J. Fitzgerald, Lt. Col. Corbett.

*National British Turkey Federation Committee.
(Courtesy of conference publication 'The Turkey Times', Eastbourne 1959)*

In 1951, Father along with John Cassidy and Roy Benton, set up the Norfolk Branch of the Turkey Federation and Father became its president until Bernard Matthews took over when Father died in 1980, a month short of his 80th birthday. Father was also a founder committee member of the National Turkey Federation with Rupert Chalmers-Watson from Scotland and other turkey farmers from across the British Isles. For many years, both Father and Mother attended the National Turkey Conferences which took place in February of each year, at either; Harrogate, Lytham St. Ann's, Eastbourne or Bournemouth.

During the year of 1953, a feed company known as BOCM, (British Oil and Cake Mills), arranged a Turkey and Breeding Trial at Stoke Mandeville, Bucks. Ten teams of turkeys sent by different competitors, arrived at Stoke Mandeville between February 17th and 20th. The teams consisted of seven breeding hens and one stag of different breeds ranging from American Mammoth Bronze, Broad Breasted Bronze and various crosses of these breeds, to the smaller British White and Beltsville Small White and Norfolk Black. All the turkeys were weighed on arrival and the hens fitted with 'Amey' turkey saddles for protection when mating. Each team was housed separately in fold units on grass, with the fold being moved each day. From March 1st for 100 days, complete records were kept of egg production, feed consumption, broodiness and any other factors of interest.

The championship was won by Peter Gallant of Legbar Farm, Taverham in Norfolk with his American Mammoth Bronze x Broad Breasted Bronze, scoring the highest total of marks for the whole trial. The award for the best feed conversion, breeding and rearing section went to the Norfolk Black team that my Father had entered. He was overjoyed to think that the breed he saved from extinction in the 1930s had become known again for its qualities of egg laying, feed conversion and moist, tasty tight white flesh on the finished bird. A 'good doer' as we say in Norfolk. From then on his passion to keep the breed alive took off. Fewer Beltsville Whites and Cambridge Bronze were reared, and Rookery Farm became the 'Home of the Norfolk Black'.

Advert for 'Broad Breasted Bronze Turkey'.

In 1953 the 10th World Poultry Congress was held in Edinburgh and I accompanied my parents for my first long car trip to Scotland. I sat sandwiched on the back seat of a new Ford 10 car between large suit cases containing practical ware for farm visits and evening dress clothes for the conference ball. The poultry papers were very intense to listen to and beyond my understanding. I attempted to be interested and felt quite important sitting with my name tag like all the others attending the conference in the Usher Hall in Edinburgh. There was a farm visit to Rupert Chalmers-Watson's and Mother was not so sure that I should

94

go along. But as we were part of the conference and Father needed to go, we were taken too. I can still remember my mother trying to guide me away from a demonstration of stag turkeys being masturbated for the semen and then men inseminating the large hen turkeys. Mother's Victorian upbringing was against letting young girls see this sort of thing. Artificial insemination is how the poultry industry have bred both chickens and turkeys with large breasts and shorter legs that put on weight very quickly. It was perfected in America in the 1950s and is responsible for the creation of the double breasted white turkey we can buy in the supermarket today.

1953, attending the 10th World's Poultry Congress
From left, Gertrude Peele, Frank Peele and Paddy Peele.
(Photo Illustrations)

The conference ended with a grand ball and I was lucky enough to still fit into the bridesmaid's dress of gold taffeta overlaid with red and gold net, that I had worn at my sister Diana's wedding in February that year. At Thorpe House School we had been taught basic ballroom dance steps. I was quite thrown when Father took me on the dance floor announcing it was a quick step and proceeded to dance the 1920s 'two step'! My toes took a battering that night!

1953, 10ᵗʰ World Poultry Congress ball.
(Photo Illustrations)

The Llewelynn family from Tenby in Wales had brought their 14 year old son along to the conference ball and after some encouragement from both sets of parents, we shyly mastered the quick step in some sort of fashion. The highlight of that trip was the Military Tattoo at Edinburgh Castle. But first I had to encounter a seven course meal before the evening event and we were driven to the Military Tattoo by a gentleman who had lost his hand in the war and steered his car with the aid of a hook. This unnerved me a bit and I was glad to get out in the fresh air after a nerve racking journey and eating such a big meal!

Father was often in demand to judge turkey farms all over the country.

Some weekends he would be away at conferences or meetings and take Mother. This left me to be looked after by Bob Curson his wife, Nell (who was the sister of Bill Abel the cowman) and Maud who helped in the house. Bob Curson came back to work for the family in 1951 and took on the job of Farm Foreman responsible for the dairy and arable side of the farm. I loved staying with Bob and Nell in their little cottage called 'Bearton House' at Welborne. It was a great novelty to go to bed by candlelight and have a big jug of warm water and a bowl to wash my face in on a washstand in the bedroom. Nell made excellent pork cheese. No doubt learnt from her father who was a pork butcher in Garveston. It was also great fun to stay with Bill Abel and another sister he called Titch. I believe her real name was Doris. She was a small homely person who never married and looked after the family. In the winter I looked forward to staying at the snug little house with its stable door entrance and western style porch veranda that covered the back door. A rainwater container, in the form of a barrel, placed to catch the soft water from the roof, stood to the right of the entrance. The house was at Riverside, Tanners Green, Garveston where Bill's father had been a butcher.

Many years before we presume the property was once the site for tanning leather. With the river near it had been an ideal site to preserve hides. The usual method was for bark of oak or fir trees to be bruised and broken in a mill and steeped in water to release the tannin giving a yellowish bronze colour to the resulting leather, hence the name of Tanners Green.

I can still remember the blazing log fire in the old fashioned grate with the blackened kettle puffing hot steam from its spout sitting on the side of the hot embers. Lighting was by a lamp on the table which gave a soft mellow light casting dark shadows across the small homely living room. My treat was to have Heinz Spaghetti on toast which tasted so good being prepared in a saucepan on the log fire. The thick wedge of bread becoming toast when held by a long handled metal fork in front of the hot flames. With lashings of butter melted into the black carbon looking toast, it was a feast for me as a hungry teenager who seemed to be starved of food at boarding school. I supposed I relished this treat as spaghetti was never on the menu at home. All our meals were always cooked from basic ingredients and only sardines or salmon seemed to come out of a tin. To get back to the farm, I would ride pillion passenger on Bill's Bantam motor bike holding tight around his waist and let the wind blow through my long hair. No compulsory crash helmets, goggles and gloves in those days!

For the Coronation in 1953, a fête and a meal were held at Garveston Village Hall and both Mother and Father were involved in its organisation. Just like at the end of the war in 1945. Mother, with other village friends put on a big spread of food for the children and Father organised the games by starting each competition with a blow on his war time whistle. These included the egg and spoon race with white shiny porcelain eggs balanced on wooden mixing spoons. The eggs usually came to grief a few steps down the course. Large thick brown hessian sacks with the corn merchants' names printed in black on the side, found children and adults struggling to run or walk to the finishing tape. I found that it was advisable to have a partner about the same size and stride for the three legged races. Fortunately, all the sports took place on grass so any tumbles were softened by the springy turf. When it came to bowling for the pig, it was a 'pip-man' piglet that was the prize. Usually some farmer would have a runt or small piglet in the litter that needed to find a home.

It was during 1953 that Father bought me Redskin. A 12.2 hand stocky red/chestnut coloured pony with a white blaze down his nose. He had spent most of his 12 years underground working as a pit pony in a coal mine pulling truck loads of coal to the surface. I spent an enjoyable week at the Dormy Hotel, Sheringham, where Redskin had been taken for retirement and for children, who stayed at the hotel to ride, before it was decided I should take him back to the farm. In that week I was to learn how to groom and clean, tack and saddle this pony and generally get to know him. Each day we had long rides with other children from the hotel to East and West Runton, past the lighthouse, and on the beach when the tide was low, then back to the hotel on bridleways well away from the traffic. I loved this area of countryside with its ferns and heathland vegetation.

Sally and Redskin.

Being a weekly boarder, Redskin was looked after while I was at school by Bill the cowman. Bill felt that Redskin should have a diet of oats and hay to give him plenty of energy. This worked very well and at the weekends I found Redskin sometimes too strong to handle! The inevitable happened and soon he was suffering from laminitis. A debilitating condition of the feet brought on by over feeding of rich food and grass.

At the local gymkhana, we both had a lot to learn, as Redskin had never been taught to jump or bend around poles. We were never very good at these events, but it did get me out in the horsey world. Now with all the litigation and insurance, health and safety worries, I feel the children are missing out on getting to know and work with animals and enjoy exploring the countryside. We can all learn a lot from studying the actions of animals. Redskin took me many miles around the adjacent villages and I was always aware that the local children, whom I had not been to school with, thought of me as that toffee nosed girl who lived at Rookery Farm. I felt that I was never part of the village gang by being sent away to boarding school.

Chapter 12

Bob's Diaries

When Bob Curson returned to the farm in 1951 and took up the position of Farm Foreman, he kept a diary of day to day events. With Bob managing the land and cows, this allowed Father to spend more time building up the turkey enterprise and going to turkey federation conferences and judging. Reading Bob's diaries from 1952 to 1985 we can see how life and costs have changed over three decades.

Rates of Pay
1952   paid £5.13 shillings per week for 43hrs work
        (½ day worked Sat)
1985   ordinary worker over 20 years of age paid £89.70 for 40 hours
        (no Sat work)
        Craftsmen for 40 hours = £103.16
        Grade 1 = £121.10 Overtime = £3.87

Farming was very traditional in the 1950s and relied on the waste products of animals to enrich the soil. Therefore in the 1952 diary, Bob has the measurements and calculations of muck all laid out. Manure was heaped in rows five to ten yards apart with similar distances between heaps as this permitted easy and uniform application and fitted in with the system of ridging practised in various parts of the country.

10 yds by 10yds = 100 sq. yards = 50 heaps per acre
5 yds by 10 yds = 50 sq. yds = 100 heaps per acre
5 yds by 5 yds = 25 sq. yds = 200 heaps per acre

Weight of heap   ½ cwt = 5 tons per acre
                        ¾ cwt = 7 ½ tons per acre
                        1 cwt = 10 tons per acre
                        1 ½ cwt = 15 tons per acre

1 cubic yard of farmyard manure weighs 12 to 16 cwt.

1 ton of bulls farmyard manure covers 1 ½ cubic yds.

The dairy breeds kept in Great Britain were Shorthorn, Friesian, Red Poll, South Devon, Ayrshire, Guernsey, and Jersey.

2 furrow plough tractor did ½ acre per hour.
15 coulter grain drill did 1 ½ acres per hour.
Binder cutting all round did 1 – 1 ½ acres per hour

Measures
4 pecks = 1 bushel
8 bushel = 1 quarter
1 bushel = 1 strike
5 quarters = 1 load or wey
4 bushel = 1 coomb
10 quarters = 1 last
(A note made on September 26th 1952: '*Corn drilled setting for Staring wheat – 12 pecks to the acre*'.

Bob's diary, written every day of the year, gives a valuable insight into what happened in each month and who did which jobs, what the weather was like, and how much and when he was paid. There were six and sometimes seven men working on the farm with extra help at harvest and Christmas.

Bob Curson - Foreman
Bill Abel - cowman
Tom Clarke - tractor driver
Charlie Page - team man, later poultry man
Jimmy Reed - general
Horace Greenwood - general
Eddie Softley - under 18

When Eddie Softley went into the army and Tom Clarke left, Reg Bowman and Billy Breeze were employed. John Thacker came to the farm in 1952 from school and retired in 2003 - 51 years later. I have included excerpts as they were written in Bob's diary in 1952 and put explanations of farming methods at the time, in brackets. In 1952, on the land it was the start of more mechanization.

3pm cup of tea.
Left to right, Reg Bowman, John Thacker, Bill Abel.

1952 Tues. Jan. 1ˢᵗ
Yard work. (Bob helped Bill to feed, water and bed the cattle with straw.) *Scrubbing turkey saddles.* (Cleaning the protective canvas saddles worn by the female turkey when mating.) *Jimmy – hedging.* (This was done with a slashing hook by hand during the winter to tidy hedges) *Tom and Eddie – manure carting.* (The muck produced by the turkeys and cows was put on a heap) *Diana got engaged to Peter Howlett of Weston Longville.*

Wed. Jan 2ⁿᵈ
Yard work and clearing cart shed.

Thurs. Jan. 3rd

Yard work and manure carting. Sent 7 turkeys to Yorkshire. 4 white hens, 3 bronze stags, 1 black cock, 1 white hen by rail. (These birds were breeding stock sent live from Thuxton Station.) *Tom started ploughing turkey meadow. Jimmy and me dung cart. Paid £6/2/- wages.* (Men were always paid on Thursday so that the wives could go shopping on Friday.)

Fri. Jan.4th

Yard work and manure carting with Eddie. Jimmy hedging, Tom ploughing turkey meadow. Mangold carting. (This would be carting mangolds stored in a clamp to be chopped up and mixed with chopped straw and fed to the cows.)

Sat. Jan. 5th

Yard work and straw carting. Jimmy trimming. Tom ploughing. (A half day was worked on Saturdays. Tom finished ploughing the turkey meadow the next Thursday with his one furrow plough behind a steel wheeled Fordson tractor. The field consisted of 16 acres and is still called the 'turkey meadow'. It was grassland when Father took over the farm in 1932 and was ideal for rearing turkeys and fattening them for Christmas. This field was ploughed up during the war to grow more corn to feed the population. During the war it was planted with linseed, a crop that was subsidised by the government. Linseed has a lovely blue flower and grows to about three feet tall with a fibrous stem. The stems are difficult to cut with a binder as they are very stringy and tough. The fibre, when processed, was used for ropes and canvas tents for the army. The plant is similar to flax which was grown during the reign of Henry VIII and Elizabeth I when each village that had over ½ acre of cultivated land had to grow flax to produce rope and sail canvases for the war ships. During the Second World War, the seed from the linseed plant was harvested and crushed for oil and the residue was dried into large slabs, which, when crushed through a cake crusher, were used to feed cattle. Maize was also grown at the end of the war on the turkey meadow. The cobs were gathered and each golden grain was taken from the cob by hand. This was a time consuming job which I gather my grandfather Ernest did, as he was unable to do any physical work on the farm.)

Mon. Jan. 14ᵗʰ
Took fat pig to Hewitt's for slaughter. (This was a butcher's shop in Mattishall.) *Scrubbed a few saddles and did a little stitching of some. Took stock turkeys to station. 17 hens and 5 stags. Eddie ditching. Tom and Jimmy hedging.*

Tues. Jan. 15ᵗʰ
Mr Peele went to Poultry Conference in London. Yard work. Straw and kale cart with Eddie. Finished ditching down front meadow. (Kale is a tall brassica crop grown and chopped up for cattle. The variety called 'Marrow Stem' had, like its name, thick juicy stems, and 'Thousand Head' had a thin stem but more leaf. Hedging and ditching was always done in January/February Ditching by spade kept a base in the bottom of the ditch and allowed the ditcher to see the flow of water, and kept the drains from the land, free of obstructions.)

Wed. Jan 16ᵗʰ
Saddling up hen turkeys for breeding. Cleared blocked drain at back of straw stacks. Eddie ditching, Jimmy and Tom hedging. Motor cycle packed up. Kirb spring dogs broken. (Bob and Bill came to work on a motor bikes. Charlie and the rest of the men came by bicycle each day.)

Thurs. Jan. 17ᵗʰ
Yard work. Carting turkeys to station. Eddie ditching, Jimmy and Tom hedging. (Any large tree branches or ash poles would be brought to the farm and made into fire wood.)

Fri. Jan. 18ᵗʰ
Jimmy day off. Yard work then Tom and I cleaning out crates in barn. (These were the crates for transporting live turkeys. The crates were usually returned by customers.) *Eddie with Charlie making folds.* (The breeding turkeys were put out to grass in movable fold units. One stag turkey with six or seven hens.) *Weston 1000 cabinet incubator installed.* (No more turning eggs by hand.) *Mr Peele took wireless recording at*

Postwick, near Norwich. (Local radio broadcasting station) *Mrs Peele fell off her cycle.* (Going downhill to the station to collect the paper, she hit a clod of mud and pitched over the handle bars cutting herself badly.)

Mon Jan 21ˢᵗ
Helped with TT test on all cattle. (All cattle tested yearly for bovine tuberculoses.)

Thurs. Jan 24ᵗʰ
Yard work. Beet carting. Ditching with Eddie. Jimmy and Tom hedging. New batteries fitted to electric light plant. (These were the storage batteries for the Ruston Hornby engine.) *Second test of TT. One probable reactor.* (A 'reactor' would have had a strong skin reaction to the TB inoculation, which would show as a lump on the neck. This probable reactor would have to be retested.) *Black Turkey Club meeting.* (Chairman, Neville Langridge a farmer at Postwick, Secretary, Harold Allsworth, a representative for Spillers Foods. He created the breeding programme for our enclosed flock of Norfolk Black Turkeys. The club disbanded in 1975. I was the last member to join.)

Mon. Jan. 28ᵗʰ
Straw cart and blood testing turkeys for BWD (BWD is short for Bacillary White Diarrhoea.)

Wed. Feb. 20ᵗʰ
Charlie away on holiday. Threshing barley from stack. 102 sacks and 15 sacks dredge corn. Tom, Jimmy and Eddie threshing. (The threshing gang that came with the Marshall tractor and machine totalled five or six men. Tom and Bob Matthews from Welborne worked for A J Farrow, a contractor from Mattishall, who went from farm to farm, threshing corn in the area. Before the Marshall tractor was used, a Burrell steam engine, driven by Tom Matthews, in his smoke and oil stained cap and overalls, would come around the tight corner, past the house pulling a threshing drum, straw walker and water cart with his bicycle hung on the back. Quite a sight to see the engine easing its way around the corner, with a little puff of black smoke and the metal wheels churning up the gravel

yard to grip the surface, with such a load being dragged behind. Tom Matthews, seemed to make handling these big machines look so easy.) *Boss and I fitted up Mead and Cope & Cope brooders in No 7 and No 8.* (The brooders have been used for over 50 years in the old wartime huts bought from Shipdham airfield. The huts were moved and erected by Cordy and son of Hingham.)

Fri. Feb. 22nd
Charlie away. Tom and Jimmy beet and manure carting. (Fodder beet or mangolds were grown for the cattle.) *Eddie, Boss and I moving stock turkeys into folds.* (These breeding folds were homemade and gave turkeys access to grass, and shelter from the weather.)

Homemade moveable fold containing breeding turkeys wearing saddles.

Sun. Feb.24th
Tom yard work morning, Eddie poultry work morning Bob yard work afternoon. (Bill usually did the milking most weekends and Father the poultry on Sunday afternoons.)

Tue. Feb. 26ᵗʰ
Straw carting, chaff cutting, grinding.(A shed next to the barn was called the chaff house and had a line of pulley wheels driven off a pulley wheel attached to a Fordson tractor, which in turn had belts attached to the wheels that drove machines to grind fodder beet or mangolds, cut straw into chaff or chop kale stalks into small pieces. Huge heaps of mixed straw, chaff and beet, or kale, plus some ground corn made into meal were taken by basket called a skep, as feed for the cows or bullocks while they were inside during the winter.)

Thurs. Feb. 28ᵗʰ
Caponized 48 cockerels. (This female hormone implant was also done on late hatched turkeys, making them put on extra weight and a better finish for Christmas. If the feathers on immature birds are not fully formed when plucking, they will leave a black stubby mess in the skin. This was one of the reasons the black and bronze turkeys lost favour with the public from the 1960s. White feathers on a turkey or capon, do not show so much. Caponization, which is now illegal, made the skin so tender that it could be easily torn when plucking. Mother seemed to spend most of her time at Christmas, sewing up torn skin with white cotton, to make the turkeys look more presentable.)

Mon. March 3ʳᵈ
Jimmy and Eddie cultivating and clearing up kale stalks on Bartrum's. Myself drilling Sulphate of Ammonia on big meadow. 20 acres in 6 hours. Could not get it on, too wet. (Bartrum's is a field once owned by Mr Bartrum and later by Mr Bone, so it has both names.)

Tue. March 4ᵗʰ
Sow had litter of eleven. Charlie away. Tom ploughing Three Corner field after kale. Jimmy and Eddie cleaning up kale stalks.(Mother kept Large Black or Essex saddle back pigs as a bit of pin money for the house. The Three Corner field is a triangular field which is rented from Garveston Charity Trustees. This area was common and heath land until it became enclosed under the government Enclosure Act. The other two fields rented from the Trustees, were called Tower field because a pylon carrying the

107

mains electricity, the Walpole line, crosses the field, and a one acre field called the Devil's Acre, so named because of its size and wet soil. This 7.5 acre area came under the control of Garveston Trustees in the Enclosure of Commons Act of 1810 when the yearly rent was collected and given to the poor of the parish, to buy coal and wood for heating.)

Thurs. March 6th
Chain harrowing big meadow. 20 acres in 4 hours. (This process was done in the spring with a dragged implement that looked like a series of metal squares with spikes on. These spikes took out the moss and gave the grass a 'brush and comb', so letting the air in after the winter.)

Mon, March 17th
Put manure on Bartrum's. 10 acres in 4½ hours. Finished off the day pitch pooling. Tom pitch pooling and boss discing kale land. (A pitch pool was an implement with curved tines that helped to create a seed bed for the corn to be drilled)

Wed. March 19th
Jimmy sowing Nitrate of Chalk on 20 acres wheat.

Fri. March 21st Drilled bean dredge on turkey meadow. 6 acres before lunch – 3½ hrs. (Bean dredge was a mixture of barley, oats and beans, bought as mixed seed, and grown to feed the turkeys.) *Valve spring broke on Allis Chalmers tractor.* (The Allis Chalmers tractor was mainly used for drilling, tractor hoeing the mangolds and pulling the binder at harvest.)

Sat. March 22nd
Had afternoon off. Went to Norwich and bought BSA motor bike for £80. Allowed £25 on Rudge. Mileage on BSA – 10,949. (Bob spent many hours on the farm with little time off.)

Mon. March 24th
Tom Clarke and Jimmy Reed hedging up 'Smee'. The boss and I fixing up Meade brooders in No 8 and marking eggs for incubation.

108

(Smee or smew is an old English word for a widgeon, or pin tailed duck. Smee drift is marked on the maps as an old unmade track. The soil in the surrounding fields is wet and sticky.)

April 10ᵗʰ
Yard work as usual, then fed the turkeys in the folds. Tom, Jimmy, Eddie and myself threshing dredge corn. 115 sacks of wheat, barley, oats and peas from 9 acres. Took straw up 'Smee' for heifers.(Heifers are young female animals that have not produced a calf. In 1951 Father bought Tudor cottage and 14 acres of land near Smee drift. This was all grassland and very wet. The field soon got nicknamed 'Lakey Hill'.)

Threshing.

Easter Sat. 1952
COWS LAID OUT. (What a joy to see the cows go out to grass after the winter months spent on cleaning, bedding and feeding each animal. They skip and jump around, tearing up the fresh green grass and tussling each other with their horns. Often ending the day with a broken horn or a bleeding wound down the side, and very tired.)

April 21ˢᵗ
Brought heifers home from Smee. Tom to start ploughing Smee with deep digger.

April 22ⁿᵈ
Yard work and turning turkey eggs. Jimmy burning up hedge trimmings on Smee while Tom ploughing. Eddie scrubbing up incubators after hatch. I took day old chicks to station. 5 fat pigs to bacon factory.

April 24ᵗʰ
Tom ploughing up 'Smee'. Jimmy in garden. Eddie, Boss and Charlie moving remainder of turkeys to folds. I pitch pooled, rolled and harrowed kale land. Drilled kale with new 'Bean Seeder'. (Jimmy helped in the large vegetable garden which contained apple and plum trees, beds of strawberries and raspberries and all types of vegetables for use in the house).

April 26ᵗʰ
Jimmy and I drilled 'Smee' – Lakey Hill with dredge corn.

April 30ᵗʰ
Yard work and folds. Jimmy garden. Tom and Eddie cleaning out black turkey yard. (This was the dung made by the turkeys which was cleaned out, by hand, with a fork.) I drilled approx. 4 acres of mangolds on Turkey meadow, 23-25 hole on seeder. Land very cobbley. Drilling not too good.

May 7ᵗʰ
Cooled milk and moved folds then rib rolled small fields on Thuxton road and rib rolled and harrowed in small seeds on Bartram's bottom 6 acres. (Small seeds is a term given to a new grass ley or pasture, for making hay the next year.)

May 13ᵗʰ
Crop sprayer arrived. Put last lot of mangolds in Three Corner field on 27 hole and harrowed in. Dusted kale with bean seeder. D.D.T. at 27 hole.

110

(The dusting was to prevent fly from attacking the young kale plants.)

May 16th
Yard work and turkey eggs. Fitted up Weedmaster on Allis tractor. Afternoon sprayed front meadow with P.30. 90 gallons water to 8 gallons P.30. (This spelt the end of the cowslips and wild flowers on the front meadow, as well as the thistles, docks and buttercups that took away the nutrients of the grass.)

May 19th
Sprayed Horse Meadow with Cornox. 2 gallons to 43 gallons water. Sprayed Big Meadow with P.30. Stayed and turned eggs. (The Gloucester and Glevam hand turned incubators, were still used, plus the automatic Weston.)

May 20th
Fitted hoes up on Allis and hoed last lot of mangolds and kale.(This loosened the ground and took the weeds out between the rows of mangolds or kale.) *Looked out hay cutter and cut piece of maintenance mixture in front of turkey folds for hay.*

May 22nd
Finished de-carb old Fordson tractor and started fitting new axle and king pins. Tom moving folds, mangold carting and turning hay. Weather hot and dry.

May 26th
Yard work and cooling milk. Took Paddy to school. (Thorpe House). *Dusted first lot of mangolds with P.P. Dust. Finished repairs on old Fordson tractor. Tom and Jimmy started chopping out kale.* (Seedlings of kale, mangolds and sugar beet, the latter, were never grown at Rookery Farm, were thinned out by hoe, leaving a single plant six to eight inches apart. Nowadays a single seed can be position drilled, so avoiding the back aching and time consuming job of singling.)

111

June 12th

Finished cutting hay. Turned hay cut first day and cocked maintenance mixture.(This was done by hand.)

June 18th

Yard work and turning eggs. Started cutting hay, maintenance mixture, part of clover mixture. Bad cutting, laid.(This hay mixture was made up of rye grass and red clover which was broadcast by hand in March/April the year before, into the already growing barley. The idea being that the corn crop would protect the small seeds from drying out in the summer, and therefore get a good establishment for the next years hay crop. The old way was to cut, and after letting the grass and clover wilt for a few days, the hay was further dried and mellowed by heaping into small cocks on the field, before they were carted to the barn or made into a large hay stack or rick. Later in the autumn, if the weather was good, the seed from the red clover would be threshed, making another income for the farm. In Norfolk, this grass area was referred to as 'the olland'.)

June 19th

Tractor hoed kale and second batch of mangolds. Cocked remaining hay. Tom and Jimmy scoring kale. Eddie cleaning out turkeys. (Scoring kale and mangolds, was a term given to hand hoeing a second time, so taking out excess plants, where doubles and weeds were growing. The tractor hoe should have loosened the soil between the rows and killed the weeds, but this was dependent upon the condition of the soil and type of weed. Mares tail, said to be a descendant of a prehistoric plant that once grew like a forest, and iron weed are difficult to kill, as the root system goes far down into the soil.)

June 25th

Boss and family went to Royal Norfolk Show. Tom and Jimmy carting hay. Bill and I shut up turkeys and turned eggs. (Mother or Father always shut the turkeys into huts at night, when the turkeys were young. Otherwise they will sit outside in the pouring rain and get chilled.)

June 26th
Bill, Eddie and I went to show. Tom did milking. (The farm workers would go to the show on the second day. The first day, was when the gentry and ladies would dress up for the show, with hats and possibly new clothes. 1952 was the first year that the Norfolk Branch of the Turkey Federation had a stand at the show.)

July 7th
Took Paddy to school. Odd jobs remainder of day. Tom and Eddie laying hoggin on roadway and Willamott shed.

1952, Mother and Father outside British Turkey Federation stand at The Royal Norfolk Show.

July 8th
Pandex shed arrived. (Father always said he put a shed up a year. The Pandex was originally for turkeys but after one year of use it was found not successful for turkeys and became a bullock fattening yard.)

Eddie cleaning incubator and Charlie milling food for turkeys, feeding and collecting eggs. (Cleaning incubator and mucking out little huts continued from April to mid July. Charlie milled the food for the turkeys, up to Christmas, from our own home-grown corn.)

July 25th
Photographer and writer came for Turkey News.

July 26th
Fetched men to put up Pandex. Eddie and Bill went to YFC Rally. (Diana was one of the first secretaries for Dereham Young Farmers' Club which started in 1943. The National Federation of YFCs was started during the war to educate young people in farming, as agricultural colleges were closed during the war. Calf clubs were formed, where young people bought a calf, fed and handled it and did all the costings, and then took it to a show to be judged. This was the start of Young Farmers' Clubs.)

July 30th
Pandex cattle shed and yard completed. Cut Bartrams 10 acres of oats. Tom, Jimmy and Eddie setting up. (Oats have a very shiny straw and would have been cut early to finished ripening on the shock. The corn was cut by a binder pulled by the Allis Chalmers tractor. The resulting sheaves were set up into shocks or stooks, by standing 6/8 sheaves leaning with the corn heads together in an A shape, and usually placed east to west, so that air went through and dried the unripe straw. According to the weather, the corn would be set up in the field between a week to two weeks, to finish ripening before being carted and stored in a stack. During cutting, the men would surround the area to catch the rabbits and game from the last piece of standing corn. Sometimes the local 'bobby', on his beat, would leave his bicycle on the side of the field, and join in. A subtle way of finding out who held a gun licence.)

Aug 1st
Mowed around Waterloo 20 acres.(Mowing was done the old fashioned way with a scythe. This was to open up the field ready for the tractor

and binder to get the first round cut, without spoiling the outside corn.) *Staring wheat cut on bottom of Waterloo. Tom, Jimmy, Eddie, Sidney, and Bill setting up.* (Bill helped in the harvest field between milking the cows and during the evening until dark. Sidney Kiddle did the post round, 15 miles on his bike in the morning, and then helped with harvest. He also helped Mother with the flower garden. Every day, at 3pm in the afternoon, Mother would make a cup of tea for all the men on the farm, plus the various reps. from firms that happened to call about that time. At harvest or when the men were working in the fields, bottles of tea were taken to the field. Then at about 5.30pm during the dry days of harvest, when everybody worked until dusk, jam sandwiches with the jam made from the green gages, plums and strawberries grown in the garden, were taken to the fields in a wicker basket, with homemade cakes and more bottles of tea. This provided a welcome rest, sitting with your back up against a corn shock on a warm summer's evening, devouring the contents of the basket. But for children, with little protection on the legs, the corn stubble left from where the binder had cut the corn, was sharp to the ankles - the only downside to the lovely memories I hold.)

John Thacker, Reg Bowman and Jimmy Reed shocking up oats.

115

Tea break time for (left to right) John Thacker, Horace Greenwood, Jimmy Reed and Reg Bowman.

<u>*Aug. 13th*</u>
Topped up second stack from 10 acre Waterloo field. (Stacks would often be built as high as a two storey house. In Norfolk from the age of 13, a tractor could be driven by a young person. This had been my sister's job until she got married, and then it became my harvest duty to drive from shock to shock, while Father or later on Reg Bowman, pitched the sheaves to Jimmy and or John Thacker, to stack on the cart. Between the shocks, and before moving on, it was my job to shout 'hold gee', a term from when horses were used. Late one moonlit night, when everyone was working until past dusk, and the sparks from the old Fordson tractor could be seen showering from beneath my feet as the tractor spluttered with its load up the hill on Bartum's, I forgot to shout 'hold gee'. Being short in the leg, I was getting tired of treading on the large metal clutch come brake to stop or ease 'granny tractor' into motion, and I started off with a jolt. I soon heard poor old Jimmy utter some words not fit for my young ears! He had nearly fallen off the load.)

116

Threshing Starring wheat off shock up Smee. 58 sacks away from drum. Slow start. Short of hands. Got stack bottom ready for Bartram's oats. Charlie helped pitch. (When making the stacks, Charlie Page, the poultry man, normally forked the sheaves off a trailer into an elevator. The corn stacks were set on a base of hedge trimmings and loose straw to keep the bottom sheaves dry. In some counties in the 19th century, corn stacks were built on a raised floor of wood set on stone piers, called 'stack stones'. This stopped the mice and rats from getting into the corn stacks. The straw from the wheat threshed during harvest, from the shocks in the field, was used for thatching the stacks to keep the wet out during winter. Stacks in Norfolk were usually oblong, but in other counties they were round.

The head of the sheaf that carried the corn, was placed to the centre of the stack in layers. The straw of the sheaf was always bulkier than the corn head and so, as the sheaves were put in layers around the stack, the middle would have to be built up with extra sheaves up to the eves. The stack was usually built so that the sides bowed out a bit to overhang the bottom and keep the rain away from the corn. Sometimes the sheaves would bow, or slip out too much, causing a bulge or 'Mae West' as Bob would call it. The bulge would have to be supported by a prop until the sheaves had settled. Bob prided himself on building stacks like a house, and I once found myself helping to fork the sheaves, from the elevator, further into the stack, for Bob to put in place. All was well until we got to topping up the stack, when I had to come out of my safe area called 'the bully hole'. I am scared of heights and I felt a panic attack coming on as to how I was going to get down from the top of the stack, as the final sheaves were set on the ridge. The ground level seemed a long way off. The elevator finally became my escape route.

Barley was the worst type of corn sheaf to handle. The harms or beards on the corn would break off and stick to your clothing. For a girl this could be very uncomfortable, especially when they ended up inside your bra. Charlie would always offer to help! Nothing was wasted from the corn harvest. The stubbles would be raked with a converted horse drawn rake behind the old Fordson tractor, to clear up any loose straw and corn. Then the cockerels, fattening for Christmas, would be put out 'to shack'. Housed in small huts on the corn stubbles, the cockerels would pick up and eat the lost grain and weed seeds.

After harvest, the farmers would descend on the Corn Exchange in Norwich, now the site of Anglia TV. The corn merchants would study the samples of wheat, barley, oats etc. by cutting the kernels of grain to see how white and dry the sample was, and how well rounded and heavy the grain weighed, before making the farmer an offer. Most large towns had a Corn Hall which resembled a stock exchange, with men in suits, standing on platforms in front of raised desks, with the corn merchants name displayed on the desk. They all seemed to be talking in loud voices to the eager farmers trying to sell corn or buy seed and fertilizers at higher or lower prices than each other. This created an air of urgency on a Saturday morning in Norwich, which coupled with the livestock market situated nearby, made Norwich come alive with the influx of country folk, and brought the sight and smells of food production to the town dwellers).

Bob Curson thatching corn stack.

Reg Bowman with yelm of thatching straw.

<u>*Sept. 3rd*</u>

Jimmy and I finished thatching stacks. (It had taken five weeks to harvest 100 acres of corn. Some days were wet and not suitable to cut or too much rain to cart and stack. When all the corn had been put into stacks, it was Bob's job to thatch each stack to keep the wet out. A heap of loose straw from threshing done half way through harvest, was wetted. Then long stems of straw were pulled and laid in bundles between two hazel sticks tied by sisal twine. This was called a yelm. Reg would take this yelm, on his back, up a long ladder to Bob, who would lay the straw on top of the stack, starting near the eves. The straw was held in place by sharpened hazel sticks called 'brorches' in Norfolk or 'spindles' in Essex, and tied across with twine. Successive layers were laid overlapping each other, until the top layers met at the peak. The ends of each stack were ornately decorated with a corn ornament or dolly. The harvest could truly be said to have finished and all was safely gathered in, when we decorated the church with produce and corn, for the Harvest service.) *Boss Charlie and Bill moved second batch of turkeys on to the 'olland'.* (The grass mixture that had been made into hay, had now grown enough to feed and free range the turkeys. The one big problem was how to keep the foxes away. It was a night time job to patrol the area or usher the birds inside huts for the night.)

Family on holiday at Gorleston.
Left to right, Diana, Paddy, Mother and Father.

<u>Sept. 6th</u>
Boss and family on holiday to Gorleston. (Every year we had a week's holiday at St. Edmunds Hotel, Gorleston. The hotel was situated on the sea front and owned by the Barfield family. As a child, the attraction of this week away from the farm was to ride the seaside ponies that paraded along the seafront and to watch the 'Punch and Judy' shows. Each year a new Enid Blyton book was bought, such as The Ring of Bells, to read if the days were wet and we were confined to the beach hut. In the early 1950s, there was quite a distance of sand to the sea and Diana and I would paddle to see the wreck of a ship partly submerged in the water. Day trips to Scroby sands to see the seals or take a small boat across the harbour to Yarmouth, or a live show at the Pier Pavilion theatre, were all very exciting. The new tarmac, on the sea front, away from the traffic, made a wonderful surface for roller skating. With my new skates, purchased from saving three penny pieces from my pocket money, I would amuse

120

myself before breakfast, skating up and down and practising my stop and turns. I never did reach the standard of those skaters who used the skating rink at the Winter Gardens in Yarmouth. Now, 60 years later this large stretch of beach has gone. The coastline has changed with the tides, and wind turbines produce power, stand like sentinels on Scroby Sands.)

<u>*Sept. 16th*</u>
Jimmy and Bill on holiday. (For several years, Bill went to a Butlin's Camp at either Clacton or Skegness. Being single, he found the companionship of other young people, and the food and entertainment, quite rewarding. It was while he was away that Father and Tom did the milking. The Alfa Laval milking machines were made with rubber tubes that had to be cut and shaped by a ring to form a round hole that the cows teat fitted into. This rubber tube was then clamped in a metal cover and attached to a claw piece by other rubbers, and then attached to a large milk tube going into a sealed bucket, which was under vacuum pressure. A small petrol driven engine produced the pressure which in turn drove a pulsator that acted like a beating heart, making the rubbers in the four cups, grip and relax, so allowing the milk to be squeezed out of the cows teats into the bucket. Every week the rubbers needed to be cut because of stretching, and the whole machine thoroughly cleaned. I had helped Bill with this job and felt quite confident I could make the required holes in the rubber liners. So one evening with steaming hot water and the various tools needed, I stripped the two bucket machines apart. Father was horrified to see his 11 year old daughter with bits of machinery all over the dairy. He had always left this job to Bill and knew very little about the intricacies of how the metal ring had to be worked in a round rubber tube to get a perfect round hole! I soon found my fingers were not strong enough for the job. It was well past my bedtime when Father and I completed the job ready for milking the next morning.)

<u>*Sept. 18th*</u>
Moved cockerels on to turkey meadow to shack.

<u>*Sept. 25th*</u>
Dressed 14 sacks of Staring wheat with Jimmy. Eddie on holiday.

(Dressing is a term used when wheat or barley seed is put over a vibrating machine. This allows the weed seeds and small grains to be separated, leaving a good plump seed for drilling.) *Mr Peele held turkey conference in Norwich at Assembly Rooms.*

Oct. 2nd

Boss, Eddie and I moved turkeys from top of Bartram's to big meadow. (They would have been walked to this new pasture.)

Oct.6th

Took holiday for one week after TT Test of all farm stock. Attleborough turkey sale. (This sale ended in 1962. A tradition that was centuries old. The only reminder of this site, is a weather vane, depicting a hen turkey with young chicks, situated on the roof of St. Edmunds Nursing Home on Surrogate Street in Attleborough.)

Oct 15th

Drilled basic slag on Abbot's meadow at 8 cwt to the acre. Tom ploughing Bartrum's top 10 acres. Eddie cleaning out huts.

Oct 17th

Jimmy and I drilled Bartram's top 9 ½ acres. Harrowed wheat in. (It took two people to drill, one on the tractor and one on the running board of the drill to check that the seed corn went out of the seed spouts evenly.)

Oct 27th

Peter caponized cockerels.

Nov. 5th

Jimmy topping mangolds. Tom and I carting mangolds. (This was a time consuming cold, muddy wet job. The leaves were cut off with a hook and left in rows to be forked on to trailers and carted to the farm yard, where they were stored in a clamp or hale. This was covered with straw to protect the mangolds from frost. The mangolds were either fed whole, about four or six to each cow, or cut up into fingers by a grinder and mixed with chaff and taken by skep to the bullocks or cows during the winter.) *Mr & Mrs Peele left for London National Poultry Show.* (This was the big poultry show held at Olympia. Father won the turkey cup for best bird in show for three consecutive years.)

<u>*Nov. 29th*</u>
Eddie finished work at farm prior to Army call up. (It was compulsory for all young men aged 18 to do two years National Service in the armed forces.)

<u>*Dec. 5th*</u>
Jimmy, governor and myself cleaning up barn. Tom poultry, kale etc. Frank Greenwood digging hole for turkey dressings etc. (The guts, after making the turkeys ready for the oven, were buried in the stack yard and covered in lime to stop disease.)

<u>*Dec. 9th*</u>
Yard work (Cattle now inside for winter) Jimmy, governor, Charlie and myself catching up turkeys – 269. Cutting up hay for calves.

Plucking Beltsville white turkeys. Left to right: George Perfect, Jack Seaman, Ken Page, and Fred Pyeman. (Photograph courtesy of EDP)

Killing and plucking all day. (The turkeys were plucked in the top of the old barn near the road. It was originally built to store and thresh corn, but Father made it suitable for doing the turkey trade at Christmas. After plucking, the birds were stumped up i.e. the small pin feathers taken out, leaving feathers around the neck and end of wings and a few feathers on the back. The birds were then put down a chute to the bottom of the barn, where they were weighed and hung on nails on wooden rails in their graded weights. The barn floor was littered with wheat straw to catch the feathers and blood that might drain from the heads of the birds. It also kept our feet warm as the barn faced north and during winter, the temperature kept below 45°F. This made it ideal for hanging poultry for ten days or so before Christmas. The only disadvantage to this old method was if the weather started cold and then turned very mild. The birds would sweat and the early plucked ones would deteriorate fast. Turkeys are game birds and as such should be hung for at least seven days to bring out the flavour. Plucking would continue until December 17th.)

Stumping. Left to right, Denny Herwinn, Eddie Softley, Horace Greenwood, Jack Frost, and Jack Ward. (Photograph courtesy of EDP)

<u>*Dec. 14th*</u>
One load of rough plucked birds to Thuxton station packed in wooden crates.

<u>*Dec.17th*</u>
Collected Paddy and Ian Salter from Norwich, after catching up chickens and last turkeys. (Most of my cousins from my mother's side came and helped at Christmas at some time during the 1950-1960s, and would all be duly housed and fed for about a week.)

Bob Curson taking parcels and crates to Thuxton Station with Allis Chalmers tractor and trailer.

<u>*Dec.19th*</u>
Odd jobs etc. Started stripping out. Tom dressing with Mother. (Stripping out was a term used to remove the feathers left on the legs, neck, wing and back. These had to be removed before dressing. i.e. making ready for the oven by removing the head, neck and insides. This job was done up the top of the barn, so all birds to be dressed were man handled up the stairs again. Mother took pride in dressing (trussing) birds. The legs

125

were broken and the sinews drawn by a hand sinew drawing machine that Father had made. The feet and legs would be washed, as they formed part of the finished weight of the bird. Some older folks liked the feet to boil up for broth. The ends of the leg attached to the bird's thigh, would be dipped in scalding water to remove the black scales from the leg piece.

Ralph Boreman with sinew drawer designed by Father.
(Photograph courtesy of EDP)

The giblets (heart and liver) would be put in the gizzard which was then neatly tied in a parcel on the neck. The turkey would be trussed with a long needle and white string. The needle went through the wing fold, then the bottom of the thigh through to the cavity to the other thigh, and back through the opposite wing and tied on the back. The wings were then folded back over the string. A second string went up through the tail end and tied the legs down into position, with the fat from the inside covering the top half of the legs. By adjusting the wings and string, a narrow breasted bird could be made to look plumper and more compact to handle when transporting.)

126

Trussing turkeys. Left to right, Eddie Softley, Fred Pyeman, Bill Abel, Mother and Ralph Boreman scalding scales on legs. (Photograph courtesy of EDP)

The birds were then carried down the stairs once more on trays, weighed by Father and put on shelves or tables. This is where the help of my cousins came in handy, and of course, me, a few years later. Somehow Mother organised food, beds for extra members of the family, plus some butcher customers who collected turkeys to take back to Bournemouth and London. Bill's sister, Maud, helped in the house with Diana. After the death of Maud and marriage of Diana, Mrs Moore and then a Mrs Beavis from Mattishall, would peel and cook extra potatoes for the pluckers to have mashed with a pot of tea at midday, as well as getting a meal ready for the family in the house. During the morning they would have already taken around to the barn on a big butler's tray; coffee or cocoa according to the men's taste, plus hunks of bread and cheese. A kettle was always boiling on the old war time Calor gas stove that stood in Mother's part of the preparation area. This kettle was used again at 3pm for cups of tea for all the men. Later in the afternoon, while plucking was in full swing, Maud or Mrs Beavis would make piles of sandwiches or hot buttered toast to go with the home made cakes that Mother had baked and stored.

Sponges with lashings of homemade jam, chocolate sponges with butter cream and scones were all taken around the barn to be eaten by workers who were there at 5pm and ready for the evening shift. Then at 8pm, there was beer for those carrying on till late evening. Sometime, Horace Greenwood would sleep the night on a sack of feathers in the barn, too tired to go home, and say he was there for any intruders. I doubt if he could have done much but give would be thieves a fright!

Evening break. Left to right: Horace Greenwood, Len Kiddle, Johnny Brown, John Thacker, Brian Bowers, Charlie Greaves, and Mike Bowers.

The longest night that Father and Bob worked was when picking the orders out for individual people and tying a label on each bird with a name, for Father treated all the orders individually. This took most of the night, usually the evenings of December 16th and 17th, when the barn was quiet and the phone not ringing. During the day it was quite noisy upstairs, with the pluckers enjoying the companionship of the Christmas activity and telling tales and jokes, some very 'blue', or singing the latest Christmas tune, accompanied by the wireless. Mother and Diana and later myself, were truly educated in a man's world during plucking time!

Working in a separate area taking the last of the pin feathers off, the men thought we could not hear, but my young ears were eager to know more!)

*Dec. 20 - 21*st

Late night wrapping birds. (The oven ready turkeys were decorated with home grown parsley pushed into the groin of the legs. The giblets and feet wrapped in individual parcels of greaseproof paper and then the turkey wrapped in sheets of greaseproof paper, and all the parcels put into a rush mat. These Chinese rush mats were then put in wooden crates. Bob or Charlie would then tie the crates down and address them ready for taking to Thuxton station, to eventually go to Liverpool station in London and all over the country. There were several firms that my Father dealt with over many years, who gave a turkey as a Christmas bonus for the staff. For years we packed turkeys for firms such as The United Paint Co. who had two factories, each was a separate order, with a list of names and weights required by each employee. These names and weights for each individual person, were put on labels of each rush mat with a list sent as to what crate number a certain employees turkey could be found. This order, as well as firms like Smeaton and Hanscombe, T.C.P. and Ince, in total about 900 birds, were packed late at night, very often stretching into the early hours. A. J. Farrow, the local haulage firm from Mattishall, would then collect and deliver to the firms in London at 6.30am.

The office work was always done by Father and no one else knew about prices charged or deals done. He personally served these firms for over 40 years until the government made a change in the tax laws, and the Christmas bonus was deemed a taxable income. By this time, my parents were both well into their 70s and Father's health was causing problems. So it was good timing when the firms decided to stop giving turkeys as Christmas presents. The Peele family had supplied turkeys to the Ince firm in London since 1905. For the next few years the family concentrated more on the individual customer and local butchers, who had been on our books for years and who came and picked up from the farm. One such firm was Leggetts of Beccles, who were fish mongers and smoked their haddock and kippers over beechwood fires and sold fresh fish from the shop. They also sold our turkeys at Christmas, which, for many years, were displayed by hanging the rough plucked birds outside the shop, until hygiene regulations stopped this practice.

Relief milker at turkey time with Alfa Laval milking machines.

Looking back, these were busy days for all. They provided money for the local workmen to buy extra family treats for Christmas, plus a turkey or chicken on the festive table. I remember for a few years, a relief milker in the form of a girl freshly out of agricultural college, would come and take on the job of milking, while Bill helped Mother with the trussing. This provided extra banter and conversation, plus scandal to be discussed by the locals who came to help with the plucking. All part of the Christmas scene.)

CHAS F. INCE & SONS LTD.
PRINTERS & STATIONERS
Established 1872

GUILDHALL PRESS

Telephone:
ACORN 2211
(THREE LINES)

DUKES ROAD,
WESTERN AVENUE,
LONDON, W. 3.

HI/JJ   14th November, 1956.

F. E. Peele, Esq.,
Thuxton,
NORFOLK.

Dear Mr. Peele,

        I find we should require Turkeys as follows, and I should be obliged if you would reserve these for us, and to quote a price for them. I presume you will supply mats as usual. The birds must arrive at Liverpool Street Station on the morning of Friday 21st December, 1956. Required: Three average about 15lbs, and 25 from 10 to 12lbs.

        We must surely be your oldest customer. I make it you have been sending us birds since about 1906 is this correct? It would be interesting to know.

Yours sincerely,
For Chas. F. Ince & Sons Ltd.,

Managing Director.

Letter from Mr Ince. customer since 1905.

Dec. 23ʳᵈ

Took turkeys to Wymondham, Norwich, Garveston and Yaxham. (Bob would do the local delivery round before Christmas Eve and then fetch my mother's sister, Rosa Salter from 10. Grove Road, Norwich where she lived. Aunt Rosa was partially blind due to a domestic accident in her early years, but liked to know what was going on around her. She always took part in the family games and sang songs around the piano on Christmas night. My childish memory of Aunt Rosa, was that she always seemed to have a drip on her nose and was forever using a handkerchief. She once said her drip had been inherited. But from which side of the family I never did find out!)

Dec. 25th
Had day off. Charlie poultry, Tom yard work morning, Jimmy yard work afternoon. Bill on all day. (The cows still required milking morning and night even though it was a holiday.)

Dec. 30th
Moving around stock turkeys. Tom and Jimmy cleaning out turkeys and putting on muck heap.

So the year of 1952 from Bob's diary, with the various seasons and the way of farming at that time completes the farming cycle. There is little mention of Charlie, who for the whole year was employed on the turkey side, feeding, collecting eggs, hatching, milling the food and then at Christmas, helping to sort and pack orders. Father employed Bob from 1951 as his farm manager, taking over the jobs of feeding calves and cattle and organising the land work. This gave Father more time to concentrate on the turkeys and general management of the farm. He did his own office work and sales, writing everything by hand on the headed paper of Frank Peele of Thuxton and attending to orders of live chicks by personally delivering them in his green Ford van. By the end of the 1950s, things in farming had started to change. Government grants were given to take out hedges and drain land, thus making fields bigger to accommodate the increased size of machinery. Food production was on the increase and so was the population. I went to Studley Agricultural College in Warwickshire in 1957, an all girls' college, to learn dairying and general farming. By the mid 1960s combines had replaced the binder. Parlours replaced the old cow sheds and men were leaving the land unable to cope with machines and the new way of farming.

Chapter 13

My Diary

Looking back through my diaries which I have tried to write up every night since 1952, I noted that my sister Diana got married to Peter Howlett, a poultry farmer from Weston Longville on February 19th 1953. I was bridesmaid with my cousin, Margaret Barnes from Fritton and gave the married couple a send off of old turkey legs tied on to the back of the car! After Diana's marriage, the usual Sunday night sing song around the piano continued for a while. Diana played the piano and Dad and I sang. Mum sat and listened saying she was tone-deaf and out of tune, but preferred to join us making our own entertainment instead of watching TV, which was still in its infancy of black and white images.

April 1st 1953. A boy called John Thacker started work. John was just 15 years old and had lost his Father. It was his uncle who brought him to the farm and asked my father if John could be of any help. One of the first jobs was to help Bill cool the milk. At first John was not strong enough to carry the full pails of milk from the cow shed across the yard to the dairy and not quite tall enough to tip the milk into the big pan on top of the corrugated water filled milk cooler without spilling some. It was not very long before John grew stronger and a bit taller from doing this physical work. This allowed Bob to do more of the land work and left John to help Bill with feeding the cows and other livestock. Wearing a maroon beret pulled down one side, John turned up for work each morning from Garveston on his push bike. Later graduating to a motor bike and then a car, during his 51 years working for the family.

December 2nd 1954. It was while I was a Thorpe House weekly border at 90 Newmarket Road, Norwich, a house owned by a lady called Mrs Arnold (who dressed in Victorian apparel with her grey shiny blue bagged hair drawn back in a bun and wearing a black high necked dress with a lace collar), that I was told my parents had lost all the poultry to 'fowl pest'. A notifiable poultry disease which is often spread by flocks of starlings or other birds, had caused the destruction of our neighbour's poultry and then ours on December 2nd. It took 2 days to kill over 3600 turkeys and 450 hens and cockerels and burn the carcasses on a fire on the back meadow. The effect on the ground can still be seen today as an area growing nettles and weeds. I remember coming home from school at the weekend and seeing the sky lit up from the bathroom window and the stench of burning flesh. Bob noted in his diary that Pettitts of Reedham sent 4 men to help with the killing. A fortnight later, Pettitts helped Father by supplying 500 turkeys for the Christmas trade. With a further 200 from George Barnes of Fritton and some from other friends, about a 1000 graced the tables of customers in London and Norfolk, a third of the planned amount. Even in disaster, Father never let his long-standing customers down. Luckily, a small nucleus of our breeding turkeys survived at a separate location and were used as the basis for restocking Peele's. An oil painting, by artist Wilfred Pettitt, of the prizewinning Norfolk Black turkey stag of 1952 was all that was left at Rookery Farm after fowl pest had struck, plus a deathly silence.

Wilfred Pettitt's brother, Victor Pettitt, started keeping poultry in 1921. By the 1950s, Pettitts of Reedham was known for supplying game and poultry meat, as well as 'feather craft' and taxidermy. This firm was the first to display quick frozen turkey at the Olympia show in London in 1948 at which the then minister of trade, Harold Wilson, took a great interest. Hilda Edwards joined Pettits after leaving school, aged 14, and worked for Pettits for over 40 years, finally becoming over all manager of the business and in charge of buying and selling poultry and advertising. In the depression of the 1930s, Victor Pettitt saw a way to make money by using the colourful feathers in hats. He employed Kathleen Edwards, who had a flair for crafting feathers and later was in charge of the feather craft side. Kathleen was not related to Hilda, but also worked for Pettitts for over 40 years. She oversaw dyed feathers, crafted into flowers and leaves and the making of artificial flower arrangements containing orange lilies, red rose buds, coloured carnations, anemones etc. all made out of feathers. Arrangements in baskets, created an everlasting blaze of colour to brighten up dull living rooms.

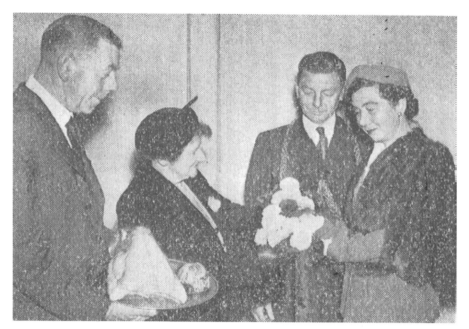

Father and Mother presenting turkey and feathered bouquet to Deputy Mayor and Mayoress of Norwich. Mother wearing her black feather hat. (Photograph courtesy of EDP)

In the 1950s, Pettitts made my mother a black turkey feather hat, which she often wore at functions. She said it was very warm to wear. In the 1970s, Yvonne Fransham put together feather designs, originally created by artist, Wilfred Pettitt. The designs on table tops, trays and pictures, were entirely made of feathers, set under glass. Even wedding bouquets and buttonhole carnations made of feathers were sold. For several years, the ladies on the top table at the annual Turkey Ball, were presented with feather carnations. The Turkey Ball was an evening's entertainment that was started by the newly formed Norfolk Branch of the Turkey Federation. In 1952, the first Turkey Dance was held at the Grovenor Hotel just off Newmarket Road, Norwich.

It was a cold snowy night in February and several guests were late. The sliced turkey and vegetables had got cold and because of this the first Turkey Ball was nearly the last to be held. Then Father suggested the next

135

ball should be arranged so that committee members could have their family and friends at individual tables, with a whole turkey for each table. The committee member would act as the host and with a chef's hat and apron do the carving. This caused consternation with some of the members as they had never carved a turkey, leaving the wife or someone else to do the deed. The next year the Turkey Ball was held at the Norwood Rooms on Aylsham Road, Norwich. The Sunshine Bakery, also on Aylsham Road, cooked the turkeys while the ovens were hot after cooking the bread. The whole turkeys were then transported to the Norwood Rooms which was attached to the Lido ballroom, where a line of waitresses, each holding a silver platter containing a turkey, would proceed across the floor to their designated table, to the tune of the 'turkey trot' played by Chic Applin's band.

President's table at the Turkey Ball, 1965.
Left to right, Frank Peele, Mrs Jones, Hugh Harrison, Gertrude Peele, Will Jones, Diana Howlett, Peter Howlett, Cath Harrison, Donald Graham, Ann Knights, Michael Knights, Pat Graham. (Picture, Royston Rowley)

After dinner we did old time dances, and took our partners for waltzes, quicksteps and even the highland fling until the early hours next day. The Turkey Ball was held at the beginning of the year when all the Christmas rush was over and a time when we could all relax. It became so popular that in 1980 when Father last attended as president of the Norfolk Branch of the British Turkey Federation, before his death later that year, there were over 850 guests dining, nearly 100 turkeys cooked and taken to tables by 150 waitresses. What a chaos there must have been in the kitchens. The dance floor would bounce up and down when we all crowded on to the floor. I was told it was suspended over a swimming pool which was covered up during the war. Since the demise of the Norwood Rooms and Lido, the Turkey Ball has been located at a hotel on the outskirts of Norwich. I can still see the evening dresses of the ladies, all trying to outdo each other with their fur capes and sparkling jewellery. The men looked so handsome and different from their daytime dress of smelly, mucky overalls and caps. This party atmosphere, plus the music and entertainment I will remember for a long time. On one occasion Rolf Harris came and sang his Australian songs using his washboard as an instrument and did his quick quirky sketches. It is good to see that a lovely tradition, started by my father, is still being carried on today.

It was fortunate that Diana married a poultry farmer. Father had put a nucleus of black turkeys at Weston Longville, where Diana lived. In 1960, fowl pest struck again, this time in the spring. All the breeding stock was slaughtered. Father later restocked with Norfolk Blacks from the nucleus of breeding turkeys at Weston Longville and stock bought back from customers. The present breeding programme stems from the four families that were obtained as replacements. Diana's husband, Peter Howlett and Harold Allsworth provided hatching eggs, Jack Frost, day olds and Roy Benton, stock hens. The blue family descended from a small holding at Ely, a new blood line to our flock. These Norfolk Blacks were small with high breast bones, and a very nervous nature and liked to fly! They were similar to the original black turkey that Father in the 1930s saved from extinction, when he and the then Norfolk poultry instructor, Mr T. D. Bell, asked for a search to be carried out to find existing stock. After great detective work a few were discovered by Mr. J. Christie's manager, the late Mr. Neville Langridge, being kept by an elderly lady in

137

an attic in North Norfolk. At that time, the breed had become rare, as the Cambridge Bronze, a larger turkey, had become more popular, and was the turkey to be found reared on farms and small holdings in East Anglia in the early 1900s.

September 1957 saw me going to a dairy college at Studley in Warwickshire after working at home and studying part time at Norwich Technical College to gain knowledge in chemistry and physics, the two subjects I was not able to study at school as there were no facilities for such subjects in those days. Farming was starting to become a whole world different from how it had slowly developed after the industrial revolution and two world wars in the 20th century. Technology in the form of science, atoms and particles, how various sprays affected plants, the use of fertilizers, plant breeding and fungicides were all to be studied as well as animal welfare and the dairy side of things. There was milk testing for keeping quality, bacteria and cell counts, modern metabolic energy and protein energy ratios for higher production of milk and the invention of milking parlours instead of the traditional cowshed. Farming and food hit a new profitable phase, with investment into machines to do the work and a different type of farmer was either trained at college or took over the family farm in the 1950s and 1960s. At college we were taught to milk by hand and machine milk and then to process the milk into cream, butter or cheese and test it in a laboratory for all manner of things from bacteria to fat content.

Studley Agricultural College was an all girls' college that taught diplomas in dairy farming and horticulture. Later in the 1960s, a farm secretarial course was introduced as the amount of paperwork and accounts started to grow with the change in farming and the countryside. The college was set in the grounds of Studley castle with parts of the castle used as classrooms and accommodation. In 1903 Lady Warwick had sold part of the estate that went with the 18th century castle and put the proceeds in a trust to educate young people in farming and horticulture. It closed in 1969 as the time had come for mixed colleges.

Studley Agricultural College and Castle. (Lionel Photography)

Dressed in green shirts or jumpers and khaki overalls, similar to what the land army girls wore during the war, we girls were expected to do and learn the farm practicalities of ploughing and sowing a corn crop, making silage and hay, threshing, (combine harvesters were just becoming more used), and looking after pigs, sheep, poultry and a herd of Ayrshire cows, plus butter and cheese making. It was during a cheese making session that one of our group of students did not scrub up properly before leaving the Stilton making cheese room, and inadvertently took the blue vein mould used in the Stilton room into the hard cheese area where Red Leicester cheese was being produced. Several months later when the large 40lb cheeses had matured, the binding on the Red Leicester cheese was taken off and revealed a blue vein of mould throughout the cheese. The students were asked to buy this cheese and take home at the end of term rather than send it to the local shop. At that time there were only the straight uncomplicated English cheeses from place names such as Cheddar, Cheshire, Leicester, Stilton etc. It seems our group of students were the first ones to make, what now is a normal trend to buy, blue veined Red Leicester or strawberry Stilton or any other additions to the old varieties of English cheese.

Looking at some of my college books I noted that a new 150 horse power Fordson Major tractor cost £650 in 1958. Now 50 years on, the Fordson name has been replaced by New Holland and a 155 horse power tractor with power steering, quiet cab, radio, satellite etc. can cost £64,000 plus VAT. In 1960 Father invested in a new petrol/diesel grey Massey Ferguson which I drove at harvest from shock to shock and having passed my driving test, was allowed to drive the tractor and corn trailer from the farthest fields about a mile away, back to the farm yard. This cab-less new machine seemed quite fast at 15 mph. and was lovely to drive on a hot harvest day with the wind rushing through my hair. The old petrol/paraffin 1930s Fordson at a top speed would only go about five mph, but with my driving, the loads were a lot safer going slower, plus the gate posts! Most fields in the 1940s and 1950s had gates and hedges to keep straying stock out. It was the custom in some places to let the cows graze the side of the road for extra fodder. Before the invention of large cattle trucks, any farmer with several cattle to move to market or to pasture, would walk the animals to their destination. In the 1800s, drovers taking cattle to pasture, would stop off at hostelries on the way such as The Bull or Ox etc.

I remember, as a child, sitting in an old model T Ford car on Ber Street in Norwich outside Smiths the butchers, when several animals of different breeds with long upturned horns came rushing past the car. Some were on the pavement and others were running down the cobbled street with drovers in hot pursuit, flailing sticks and shouting. These animals were being driven from Norwich market, which was held on a Saturday near Norwich Castle, down to the holding meadows at Trowse Station, where they would be loaded into livestock wagons and transported all over the country.

When I had finished agricultural college in 1959, I joined Wymondham Young Farmers Club in Norfolk. The YFC national motto is 'good farmers, good countrymen, good citizens'. There I met up with people I had known at Lyndhurst school in my earlier years. One person was

Roger Peacock, the son of Geoffrey Peacock who had bought Bess, the Percheron horse from my Father. He was vice chairman of Wymondham YFC and was keen to find extra members for the club. Within six months of joining I found myself taking part in public speaking, hockey, stock judging proficiency tests and many other competitions and wrote the original score for the YFC anthem.

Every Monday, meetings took place at the St. John's Ambulance room opposite the Post Office on Middleton Street. Over 60 of us would pack into the small hall to hear talks and demonstrations ranging from foot massage to crop husbandry. Outgrowing this meeting place, the club moved to the top room of the Queen's Head pub in Wymondham. Visits to farms and factories were arranged for the summer months and demonstrations on stock judging of dairy cows, beef, sheep and pigs all came into the programme as well as mock farm and antique auctions. The bidding at auctions was often way off mark for items such as tractors and combines, but the girls usually had a better eye for house hold antiques. Thank goodness no real money changed hands as the bank manager would not have been impressed!

For several years Eastern Area YFC holidays were organized by Bill Coates and Gordon Moseley. Educational visits were made to countries such as Germany, Austria, Channel Islands and Denmark. It was in 1960 that ten of us from Norfolk and mostly Wymondham YFC, took a holiday to Denmark, joining up with clubs from all over the Eastern Area, visiting bacon factories and farms. It was on this holiday that I met my future husband Donald Graham from Essex. He was in the Harlow Young Farmers and lived at Nazeing. Club members came from all walks of life and this is still the case today. But in the 1960s, the boys were mostly farmers' sons or connected to the countryside. My limited cooking skills were improved during the four years I was in the club by taking classes in cake, bread, jelly and jam making to gain proficiency certificates which all counted towards the NFU Trophy. This was the main cup that all clubs like to win at the end of the year. Sometimes the boys had a go at baking classes often producing sponge cakes that rose up thicker than ones made by the girls.

Club Dinner at the Mayfaire Suite, Norwood Rooms (Jan. 1962), when I received the Stock Judging Cup for the club from the Lady Mayoress of Norwich. In the picture, left to right, Richard Phillips, Alan Alston, Lady Mayoress, Lord Mayor, Paddy Peele, Dennis Eagle, Pat Phillips, Ann Kirchen (Photograph courtesy of EDP)

When it came to bread making, the boys attempts had a grey look where the grime of a day's work with oily machinery left the boys' hands to become embedded in the sticky dough! It was all good fun and added points to the club. At the end of the evening the edible cakes etc. were consumed at the Windmill pub and washed down with a few drinks. There was no drink/drive ban in those days and much less traffic.

To appease the boys, some of the girls took tests in cattle handling and beet singling. My attempt at singling sugar beet by hand hoe was not passed at the first attempt and had to be taken a second time. The first test was taken on fen soil, where the weeds and a good crop of sugar beet grew like a hedge, making it a time consuming job to leave one single plant. Proficiency test schemes were one of the first ways in helping those working on farms to gain recognition of their training and so get an increase in wages. This did not apply in my case as working at home there was no scope for me to get a wage increase. I had by this time obtained the first gold badge to be awarded to girls for proficiency tests in Norfolk. There were many enjoyable experiences in the four years at Wymondham YFC which took me to Olympia judging dairy cows for Norfolk, representing England in Sweden at the 4H rally in 1963, writing and performing the original YFC anthem on Anglia TV and ending up as deputy club leader.

Young Farmers taught me many things, how to work with and organize others, public speak, act as secretary and learn whilst having fun. It is an organization that is still going strong today. The introduction of the Countrysiders, a junior level of Young Farmers clubs for youngsters from all backgrounds aged 10-15yrs, started by Francesca Broom and run from the Norfolk YFC Rural Support Centre, Easton College near Norwich, has ensured that young people can continue to learn about the countryside. May these clubs teach our youth the values of being a 'good farmer, good countryman and good citizen'.

Poem written for the YFC yearly magazine 1962-63
'One of Those Days'

I've recently had the pleasure
of a monotonous daily task.
'Please milk the cows'; said Father Peele
'That's simply all I ask'.
While Bill's away on holiday
The cows must still be milked,
For profit from a dairy herd
Is valued just like silk.
So Bill, he went to Butlin's
To spend his well earned rest,
While I got up at early hours
To start my job with zest.
The cows behaved quite well at first
Until the day it rained

When through the mud up to farm
They simply would not deign.
The rain it rained the whole day long
And made my temper frayed.
Much worse when after dinner came
No power, and I delayed.
At half-past four we got a start
About an hour late.
To rush this job was my intent
For I had got a date.
Not so the cows, for sodden wet
From standing in the rain
They jiffled and they messed about,
Why did they so complain?
My favourite cow, Priscilla
Who is really quite a dear.
Tossed her head and kicked at me
A full blow on the rear.
The old cow Tess, so stayed and starched
Was in a bad mood too,
She stretched her legs, then made her aim,
Machine to door, then through.
On picking up the pieces
Of a somewhat wrecked machine,
I found a pipe was split in two,
My words were bad and mean,
The milk was down that afternoon,
Well, not to be wondered at.
When three great jars were left to fill,
Besides the flippin cat!
With aching limbs and wrinkled brow,
I struggled through that day.
So glad to see the cows go out
On pastures there to play.
Milking done and cleaned up too,
A bath I had in mind.

But air and noise came from the taps,
No water did I find.
With harassed mind, I went to club
To do my duties there.
And took the milk which I had got,
But found it quicker to draw BEER!

Chapter 14

Broadcasting and 'The Archers'

In 1960 Gordon Moseley had left as organizer of the Young Farmers Club and taken a job with the BBC doing early morning visits broadcasting from farms in a programme called 'Farming Today'. Rookery Farm featured in one of these programmes in June 1960. The programme was broadcast for the whole week from the farm going live on air at 6.30am and 7.30am.

'Farming Today'. Left to right, sound engineer, Father, Gordon Moseley, Mother, Bob Curson and Bill Abel.

The control centre was set up in the kitchenette as we called the utility room next to the kitchen. Here the telephone wires were linked to the microphones placed about the farm and at 6.00 am a test run was done with a link up live to the studios in London. From there it was broadcast all over the country. Bill Abel, the cowman, was busy getting the cows tied up in the cowshed on the morning when an interview was to take place in the cowshed. Unknown to Bill, during the evening before, the microphones had been put in place and being a lovely sunny morning, Bill struck up with a song that was all the rage at that time, entitled, *'What did Della wear boy, what did Della wear?'* This was heard in the studio in London, fortunately on the test run. The reply came back *'Ask that chap, what did Della wear last night?'*

Godfey Baseley's home at Fockbury. (From Christmas card)

As the farm was a mixed farm with cows, beef, turkeys, arable and a few pigs, the daily radio interviews during the week, covered several topics of farm life. This was not the first time that Rookery Farm had been on air. In 1950 on Christmas Day, a programme went out live from the farm when Godfrey Baseley interviewed all the family. We were placed in a line near the stock turkeys so that listeners could hear that not all the turkeys were killed and on their Christmas plate! Father talked about the work to get a turkey reared up and ready for Christmas, Mother about plucking and trussing, sister Diana about the packing and I chipped in that my job was to tie up the giblets. As an 11 year old, I found that Christmas most exciting, but Mother must have been exhausted. She had been involved in plucking and trussing several hundred birds and organising food and beds for helpers and then cooked for the family plus the broadcasting crew - turkey of course. It was then that Godfrey Baseley, who was a friend of the family, told us he had written the first episodes of a new serial for radio called 'The Archers' which was to go on air early the next year, 1951. He had based his characters on his brother-in-law and sister who lived at Summerfield Farm, Bromsgrove in Worcestershire and on various friends like my parents.

'The Archer Family'. Left to right, Dan, Doris, Jill, and Phillip.

In 1958, while I was at Studley College, Godfrey Baseley invited me to stay with him and his wife in their converted barn at Fockbury. He showed me his writing room, where every character he had written into the script had a special folder with details of hair and eye colour, height, likes and dislikes, friends, places visited etc. so that the listening public would not trip him up over detail of the characters. That weekend, the actors were being photographed for the local Archers paper called 'The Borchester Echo'. We went to Godfrey Baseley's brother-in-law's Summerfield Farm, near Bromsgrove, where the pictures were being taken. Of course

I took some photos of my own.

The imagination plays tricks with the mind and as a young girl I had built up an image of Phil Archer being a tall handsome young farmer. In the script he was the son taking over the farm from his father, Dan Archer. When I saw the actor playing the character of Phil Archer in real life, I was most disappointed. He was shorter than I had imagined with glasses and walked with a slight limp. But his voice on radio still made the character of Phil Archer quite pleasant. It was like the old saying, *'what the eye don't see the heart won't grieve over'*.

'The Archers' cast.
Left to right, Tom Forrest, Jimmy, unknown, Ned, farm owner.

After the photo shoot, we all went to the local pub for a 'ploughman's lunch'. There I met Gwen Berryman who played the part of Doris Archer. She was a lovely warm homely person and played a typical farmer's wife of that era. In real life she was also an opera singer. Later that year I arranged for her to give a talk to the Music Society at Studley College. How wonderful that a serial started so long ago is still running and

149

keeping up with the relevant farming issues of today. If the writers still continue to keep files of their characters, the folders must now fill several filing cabinets!

In 1962, Gordon Moseley was back at Rookery Farm again. This time to take a black and white silent film for BBC TV. Father and I had to go to the BBC studio at All Saints Green, Norwich, and talk over the film as it went out live on TV. This was quite a harrowing job as we could not overrun the clips of film with comments to describe what the viewer was seeing.

Chapter 15

Changing Times

September 26th 1964 saw Don and I get married at Thuxton Church with the reception at the farm in No. 7, one of the ex-army huts that came from Shipdham airfield and had been conveniently rebuilt in what was once an orchard near the house. By then a rock garden and greenhouse had replaced the formal garden that Cecil the postman and part time gardener had years before spent many hours planting with salvia, tagetes and variegated geraniums to give a blaze of colour. The rock garden and patio with water running over the rocks made a wonderful setting for the formal hand shaking before the meal of our wedding.

Wymondham Young Farmers being received at our wedding reception. (Frosdick Photography)

For part of the year, No. 7 acted as an incubator and brooder shed. Being positioned near the garden and front of the house, it also acted in the 1960s as an ideal place to provide tea and cakes during the annual Conservative garden party in July. The local Conservative candidate, Paul Hawkins, an auctioneer, who later became known as Sir Paul, would come and give a talk on the lawn and then go for tea in No. 7. The turkey brooders inside

151

the shed were cleaned down and placed so they formed a long table. Covered with white sheets to act as tablecloths, the brooders became ideal for setting the many cups and saucers on and pouring tea. It was always a very pleasant and friendly afternoon. The ladies all turned out in their best summer frocks, wearing hats as fashion decreed at that time. The small children would play on the large grey rocking horse which was supposed to be a replica of one used by our present Queen Elizabeth and her sister Margaret. Our rocking horse differed. In my enthusiasm as a six year old to groom and keep the rocking horse tidy, I had cut the flowing tail off, leaving an untidy stump, much to my parents' annoyance. Bowling on the lawn for a turkey was quite popular. The bowling board was made by my father out of apple wood. The old orchard, part of Bartrum's field, was disposed of at the end of the war. After the plane accident at Garveston, the tree stumps were used to fill up the bomb holes on the front meadow. The board is still being used today, with the high, number 9, being reinforced several times!

Jack Seaman watching Mr Woolston bowling for a turkey at the Conservative party.

In the early 1960s, the farm staff on 157 acres of arable and grass, plus cows and poultry, totalled six men, plus myself and Father. We had a woman help in the house about two days a week and the postman, Cecil Kiddle came to help in the garden and at harvest time. Spring cleaning was my mother's ritual. Her full name was Gertrude Janet and as a child, her sisters called her 'dirty Gerty'. She told me that they once put her down the old-fashioned toilet. All her life she strived to keep a tidy clean home to prove she was not a 'dirty Gerty'. On a dry spring day, all the furniture was washed with vinegar and water to take the grime and excess polish off before re-polishing and treating any woodworm. The rooms would be cleared of furniture and the carpets and underlay removed to the lawn where they were duly beaten and dragged on the grass and left during the day to revive the colour. Floor boards were then scrubbed on hands and knees with hot water and carbolic soap and windows and paint work cleaned. The windows were cleaned with damp newspaper. Then the ritual of tidying the drawers and cupboards before putting everything back. This was the way the Victorians looked after their houses. A necessary spring cleaning job after the dust from winter fires.

When I got married my parents were wondering if they would carry on the farm. The turkey industry was getting bigger and was destined for huge expansion. With no son to take over, Father decided, at his age, not to spend money on increasing the hatchery side. The housewife's taste was changing, wanting a cleaner, easier way of life. With the installation of electricity all over the country came washing machines, electric ovens and electric heaters, instead of dirty fireplaces and stoves. This clean culture brought in the fridge and freezers to keep food. There was no need to cook each day. The black and bronze turkey, with the dark unsightly stubs at Christmas, was frowned on. The white plumper breasted turkey, produced en mass by the likes of Bernard Matthews, was all the rage and soon became the everyday meat. The unsightly stubs of white feather on immature birds are not so noticeable on the modern turkey or chicken. Gone was the traditional feast of turkey just at Christmas. Gone was the flavour and old ways of treating what once was a game bird. Gone too was the meat and cream cheese etc. kept in a wood and wire construction called a safe sitting in the garden in the shade of a tree, or milk in cold water on a cold marble slab. The fridge had been developed for this job, which was here to stay and change our eating habits and way of living.

Changes also took place at Rookery Farm. With the farm staff getting older and the availability of extra labour at threshing time becoming a problem, the inevitable happened. In 1966 a second hand Massey combine was bought. Mother was certain the turkeys would not do so well on the fresh combined corn, but things had to change. A few years later, Jimmy Reed retired and Reg Bowman stopped work with back trouble. The cows were sold in 1972 after Bill was taken ill with a brain tumour. Charlie Page retired, leaving John Thacker, the youngest of the staff to take on the poultry. In 1974 Father had health problems and the membership of the Black Turkey Club dwindled and was disbanded. In 1976 trios and groups of Norfolk Blacks were sent to the Royal Agricultural Society grounds at Kenilworth in Warwickshire, Riber Castle in Yorkshire and other places all over the country to keep the breed alive. A small nucleus was retained at Rookery Farm so that contact was not lost with the ageing regular customers who had become friends of the family.

Bob Curson with combine. Note the lack of a cab.

It was always hoped that a grandchild would be interested in the turkeys and one day pick up the business and start again. After the death of my father in 1980, John Thacker with the help of Bob Curson, continued to look after the farm. Mother helped to pluck and truss about 450 birds up to her 85th year. When the barn stairs became too much to climb after having a second hip operation, she gave her advice and help from the comfort of the kitchen. The office work and turkey orders had fallen to me to do. Bob Curson continued to work the land until 1985, when he too was confined to a spell in hospital and forced to retire from full time work.

This left John Thacker from the original staff who for the next few years was the only employee. Helped by my husband Don, who did the land work, John found himself in charge of the live stock and having to do simple tasks on the land until Bob got well enough to help out at busy times. John worked for 51 years on our family farm and still gets called upon at Christmas. My knowledge of turkeys and diseases was limited, not like my sister who had married a poultry farmer and had always been inclined to that part of agriculture. I soon found myself having to take on the mantle of Peele's Turkeys after Mother's death, in 1989 and now get referred to as Mrs Peele!

Chapter 16

The Media

It was during 1989, that I did an interview for a Sunday paper about the virtues of the black turkey compared with the large 'bootiful' white Bernard Matthews' Norfolk turkey as advertised on TV. Until this time, the double breasted white turkey was all the post war general public had seen in super market frozen cabinets. A reporter from a national newspaper had seen an article written by Michael Pollitt in the farming section of our local Eastern Daily Press paper, about the Norfolk Black turkey being a rare breed. This prompted an interview from the Sunday Times Newspaper reporter. As Mother was not well at the time, I gave my home telephone number as the contact.

Due to a change of reporters in the national newspaper, the article about the black turkey was not printed that year. It was the next December, 1990, that my phone rang while I was milking cows in the morning at my home in Carleton Rode. A lady from Yorkshire had read the Sunday newspaper and was phoning to order a turkey! This was news to me, as I had forgotten about the article. This started Peele's once more sending turkeys all over the country at Christmas. It seems as though someone had found the report originally written in 1989, and thought it would be a 'filler article' before Christmas 1990. Fortunately, we had reared extra turkeys, as it was that year, 1990, that fund raisers for the church in Attleborough had asked me to provide a flock of turkeys to walk through the streets of the town, re-enacting the days when turkeys were walked to market. Someone informed the Royal Society for the Prevention of Cruelty to Animals about this fund raising event who claimed it was a 'cruel stunt' to walk turkeys. The organisers had consulted the local vet who was very knowledgeable about the capabilities of the Norfolk Black turkey. The RSPCA were thinking of the mass produced white turkey that is too heavy to walk any distance.

The local paper had headlines that a certain shop in Attleborough was telling customers to boycott the event as it was cruel to walk turkeys in this way for fund raising. With such feelings against the walk and also knowing that a military band was due to march and play behind the turkeys, the full 150 turkeys due to walk from Queens Square, got reduced to just 30. These were mostly cock birds, as it was felt that the females would be more flighty and might fly and hurt young people in the crowd. The day started with sniffer dogs and men inspecting the drain covers etc. on the route in case of a bomb attack on the military band, as this was the time when the IRA bombing campaign was at its height. Ken Clabburn of Attleborough Poultry Farms, who was used to handling white turkeys, had volunteered to transport the blacks for the fund raising event. He nervously arrived with just 30, leaving the rest at the farm and carefully handled each one out of the trailer, putting them on the grass on the small green square in front of the now Town Hall.

The drovers who took part in the turkey trot.

1990 fund raising turkey walk at Attleborough. (Photograph courtesy of EDP)

Here the town sign displays brushes from the time when the town was famous for its brush factories and turkeys from the annual turkey sales held in town. Our black turkeys took no notice of the TV cameras rolling and children trying to touch them. They were too busy pecking away at the grass and picking up cigarette ends and bits of silver paper left on the green. As the walk progressed with several of us dressed in old coats and hats with long canes to guide the turkeys through the crowds, one turkey took the lead and followed behind Ken Clabburn and a policeman who were walking in front on the road to the Connaught Hall. When the first turkey came to the pedestrian crossing by the church with the yellow lines on the road, it stopped and the others all did the same. It was quite an amusing sight. Who says animals are dumb! The whole event went well and the Lions Club, with their collecting tins, extracted several pounds from the crowd to help towards building a day care centre and meeting room on St Mary's church at Attleborough.

Rookery Farm with its black turkeys, has been featured several times on the TV farming programmes and in documentaries. Paul Heiney came to the farm and filmed a feature that showed black turkey chicks being taken from the incubator in his series of 'Victorian Summers'. Once when I was interviewed for a farming programme, the new camera with sound and film incorporated, went wrong. After several attempts at the interview and the interference of aeroplane noises, the turkeys who had been fed with corn at each take, were too full to even bother about pecking. The recording had taken most of the day and when seen on television it lasted about five minutes. The content had been edited and changed, and what was discussed, came over in a completely different way, illustrating the power of the media, and how it can influence the listener.

A similar content change happened in an article in December 1997, when a report was written in The Times Weekend paper. The heading was of *'Talking turkey with Mr Bootiful'* and displayed a picture of white turkeys superimposed in front of Bernard Matthews at his Great Witchingham Hall in Norfolk. The article describes how at the age of 20, he paid £1 for 20 hatching eggs and how his business had expanded so that in 1997 he was worth £70 million. My father helped him when he was first married and lived in a bungalow at Taverham, keeping turkeys in his conservatory. Bernard then bought the dilapidated Great Witchingham Hall for £3000 and filled the 35 rooms with turkeys. They were hatched in the dining room, reared in the Jacobean bedroom and slaughtered in the kitchen. So the Matthews empire began. Later in 1958, he bought the first of many disused aerodromes and put up large turkey rearing sheds. Great Witchingham Hall becoming his home and the headquarters of today's business.

Wedding at Thuxton Church, September 26th 1964. Donald Graham to Patricia Peele. Best man, John Graham. Bridesmaids, (in yellow) Marion, Christine and Ruth Howlett, (in red) Ann Lewin. Pageboy, Robert Graham.

Free range Norfolk Black turkeys, reared by George Barnes, Old Hall Farm, Fritton.

Norfolk Black stag turkey, hen and chicks.

Norfolk Black stag turkey, painted by William Pettitt.

Kathleen Edwards creating feathered flowers at Pettitts of Reedham.
(Photo reproduced courtesy of Pettitts)

Feathered table top.
Norfolk Black turkey feathers have been used to create the dark background.

Conservative party in no. 7 brooder shed.

Early 1960s, flower garden between incubator shed and no. 7.

Harvest threshing off the 'shock'.

Mum serving tea from the pail to threshing workers.
Cecil Kiddle (postman) on left, Bob Curson on right.

Harvest 1963, finished stacks.

1963, winter threshing.

1930s, Hugh Harrison's first bagging combine near Brandon Parva church.

1990, Bob Curson on Massey 506 combine.

Pluckers celebrating Mum's 87th birthday. Left to right, Bob Curson, Mum, Trevor Kiddle, Pat, Richard Barker, John Thacker, Peter Howlett, Paul Brown.

1990, turkey trot through Attleborough.

'Taste of Anglia' stand at the Royal Norfolk Show 2002.
Pat Graham and Bernard Matthews.

James Graham talking to Prince Charles at 'Taste of Anglia' stand,
Royal Norfolk Show 2004.

August 2002, James Graham and Rick Stein filming for 'Rick Stein's Food Heroes'. (Image copyright Peele's Norfolk Black Turkeys)

2010, James Graham and Michael Portillo (centre) with film crew from 'Great British Railways'.

John Thacker and Pat Graham putting young turkey poults to bed.

2009, Thuxton church fete.

2009, James Graham with Norfolk Black stag turkey (Image copyright Peele's Norfolk Black

Thuxton village sign.

On the same page as the article about Bernard Matthews, but under these details, was an article written after an interview with me, and headed, *'The welcome return of a really tasty turkey, the Norfolk Black'*. I had explained to the reporter, Sally Smith, that the large white turkeys were bred by artificial insemination as they were too heavy to mate properly, where as the old fashioned breeds like the Norfolk Black, still retained the shape of a game bird and could breed normally. To my surprise when I saw the paper, the caption over the top of the article and photograph of me holding a hen turkey was *'Too overweight even to mate properly'*. Was she alluding to me?!

In the early 1990s, when new regulations on health and hygiene were introduced, backed by EU law, it was necessary to upgrade our Christmas business. The barn was deemed not suitable, as the birds were hung on nails on wooden whitewashed beams in the bottom of the barn. The way it had been done for over a century. We were forced to build a new shed with a large walk in freezer or face going out of business. The whole process of killing, plucking, holding and eviscerating was to be on the level and in a line. The finished birds had to be held in another cold room, once part of the cowshed. The existing barn, used for many years, now acts as a museum and shop.

In 1989 our son James had completed college and was interested in the farm and the turkeys. Rookery farmhouse had remained empty after the death of Mother and so James moved in to take over the turkey business. It was a complete change of thought and way in doing things in the new cold store. I had worked all my Christmases in the old barn, seeing the turkeys hung individually, each labelled with a weight and name and hung to let the air circulate around the body of the birds. The temperature in the new store was down to 3-5°C with fans blowing cold air. The height of the hooks and weight of some of the cock birds, made it a struggle for me to pick out orders and hang the birds in ordered groups. After the second year of getting cold hands, feet and a very cold head and face, plus aching back and arms, I gave over to James to run the Christmas business and I now help by answering the phone, doing the office work and occasionally helping on advertising stands at the 'Taste of Anglia' events. It was at the Royal Norfolk Show in 2002 while on our Peele's Norfolk Black Turkey stand in the Taste of Anglia Food Hall, that I met up again with Bernard Matthews, who was the show president for that year. Two years later, James was on the stand, and had the honour to be introduced to Prince Charles, the Norfolk Show president for 2004. Prince Charles remembered seeing black turkeys being reared on the estate at Sandringham.

James has experienced the ups and downs of farming with scares of foot and mouth, bird flu, blue tongue, low grain prices and the many restrictive regulations that have been applied to all industries over the last few decades. No wonder I, and possibly you, the reader, feel as though we go around in circles chasing bits of paper and getting little manual work done. Unlike the organised hive of bees. Each with their required job to do at a specific time in their short lives. No paper trail here. Just collective organisation.

The Peele family tree shows graziers and farmers back to the 1660s who all experienced good and bad times, wars and depressions. James, like his great grandfather Ernest, grandfather Frank and myself have all seen these times and experienced the power of photography and media. In 2002, as well as Paul Heiney with his 'Victorian Summers' series, James and the farm were featured in a programme with Rick Stein, the well known TV chef. The most recent TV appearance has been with Michael Portillo on 'Great British Railways' on BBC 2 in January 2011 when James, Bob Curson and myself, took part in remembering the years when Thuxton Station and the railways played a part in the everyday life of the farming business.

In 2009 Peele's Norfolk Black turkeys were mentioned in Delia's cook book, 'Delia's Happy Christmas'. This has helped generate business in the form of eggs or finished oven ready turkeys as far away as the Isles of Lewis and Shetland in Scotland. A book, due to be published in 2011 called 'Mrs Beeton - How to Cook' by Gerrard Baker also mentions the Norfolk Black turkey and celebrates 150 years since Mrs Beeton published her first recipe book.

When someone takes the trouble to phone or write with their comments after Christmas, it makes all the hard work worthwhile. Naturally we like to hear the favourable ones! Occasionally there are times when sending boxes of oven ready turkeys to individual customers at Christmas can be a headache, especially if they do not arrive on time. In one instance a parcel got delivered to the wrong address where the occupants were away for the weekend. On returning they found this suspicious white parcel outside their door and informed the police thinking it could be a bomb! Fortunately the mistake was spotted by an off duty policeman whose mother was expecting this parcel and went to the rescue.

What does the future hold for farming and the turkey industry? Everything seems to be getting bigger, but at a cost to the smaller producer. Supermarkets have brought things to one level, the cheapest on offer to the consumer. Small producers still have to battle with the elements and bureaucracy whatever size of business. It seems the only way to survive is to have a niche market and sell directly to the public. The rare breeds of animals and birds can still find a place in this market as they have done through the last century. After all, they once roamed the countryside and were kept by feeding on the fruits of nature. They still have the genes and ability to survive in harsh conditions that the 'improved' man made species find difficult to live in without the back up of medicines and special food. Society in this country has become over sensitive to everything around it, overfed and overweight. We tend to try to push the boundaries of survival from small babies to injured animals etc with drugs and medicines to prolong life. But whatever new vaccine, spray or medical method that is used, God and Mother Nature will find a way to let the creatures they want to survive, adapt and change, to continue this changing and evolving earth.

Thinking back to my grandmother Eleanor's bible, we are reminded,
'The Lord is the everlasting God. He created all the world. He never grows tired or weary and no one understands his thoughts.'
Isaiah, Chapter 40, verse 28

Appendix

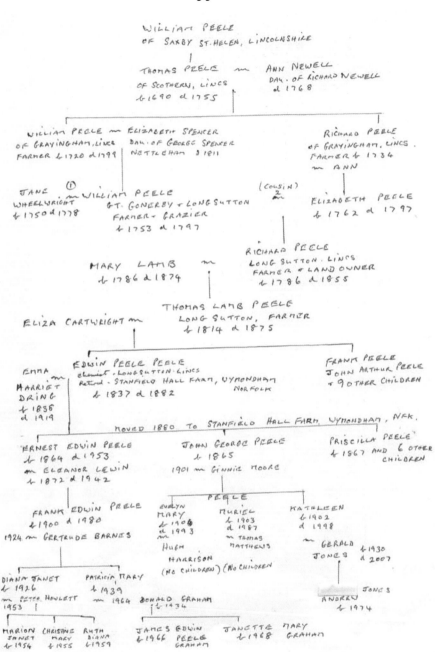

Peele family tree.

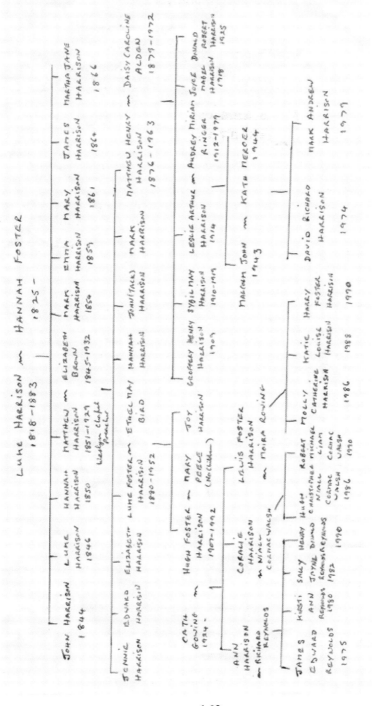

Descendants of Luke Harrison.

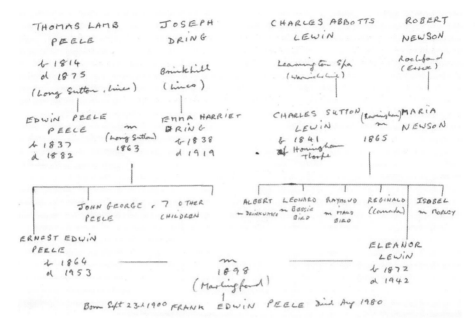

Ancestors of Frank Edwin Peele.

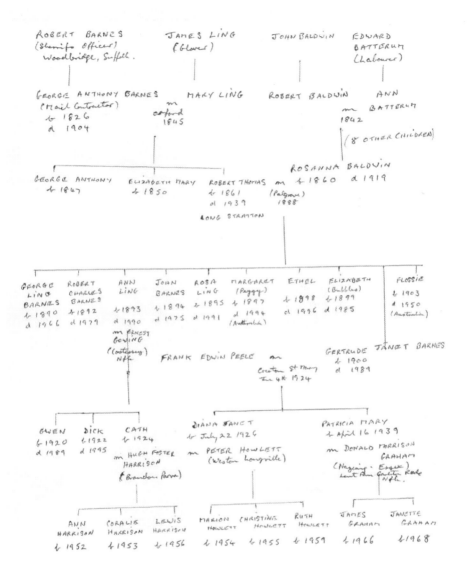

Barnes family tree.